Praise for Peter Wylie and *Data Mining for Fund Raisers*

"Peter Wylie's book makes statistics digestible and the application of modeling techniques to your fund-raising strategies a reality, and even fun!"
— *Laurent (Lo) de Janvry, Associate Director, Strategic and Direct Marketing,*
University of California, Berkeley, University Relations – Annual Programs

"No one seems to get more excited about statistics than Peter Wylie, and I suspect no one hates statistics more than I. Fortunately, Peter's approach is easy to follow and his enthusiasm for his student's success makes the process understandable and enjoyable."
— *Leah L. Zueger, (former) Associate Development Officer,*
Development Research, University of Minnesota Foundation

"Data mining can help you uncover your most likely prospects, discover major gift prospects, and craft an annual giving program that can more effectively segment your prospects. Peter Wylie makes statistical analysis of your database understandable."
— *Billie Sue Schulze, Program Director, The Kresge HBCU Initiative*

"Peter Wylie has taken a subject that can be very difficult and made it seem fun and easy to use. He has provided individuals working in both the annual fund and in research practical examples to use in their work."
— *Tricia Ambler, Director of Prospect Research, Virginia Commonwealth University*

"Peter Wylie's book is an excellent step-by-step guide to get data mining newcomers started, as well as to remind seasoned professionals how essential this tool can be to their programs."
— *Kimberly Stevenson Parks, Director of Annual Giving, McDaniel College*

"You get what you measure. As not-for-profits we need to dedicate ourselves to measuring the effects of our strategies and align our valuable resources to those strategies that maximize our returns. The measure of this book is how simple and effective a process Peter Wylie has developed and outlined."
— *Ray Satterthwaite, Associate Vice-Principal, Advancement,*
Chief Development Officer, Queen's University

Data Mining for Fund Raisers

How to use simple statistics to
find the gold in your donor database
(even if you hate statistics)

A starter guide by Peter B. Wylie

COUNCIL FOR ADVANCEMENT
AND SUPPORT OF EDUCATION.

1307 New York Avenue NW
Suite 1000
Washington DC 20005-4701
www.case.org

Table of Contents

Foreword

Something interesting is happening in the world of advancement research. After the Internet revolution, when the field of advancement research changed dramatically, there was somewhat of a lull. Researchers continue to refine their skills, but there haven't been many new BIG ideas. Technology continues to change, and researchers are on top of it.

Lately, however, there is a revolution in the works. When you listen to the conversations that researchers are having online and at conferences, the subjects of data mining and predictive modeling are coming up more and more often. People want to know about it. What is it? How can I use it? HOW DO I LEARN TO DO IT?

Haven't researchers been talking about data mining for ages? Well, yes and no. Yes, data mining has been a conference topic for as long as researchers have had data. But no, these recent conversations are about a different kind of data mining. Data mining is not just about finding individual wealthy prospects. *This* data mining is about truly understanding your prospect pool and even predicting your prospects' behavior. It's about providing sophisticated analysis that can inform and improve fund raising programs and processes. It's about providing knowledge that informs strategic planning—knowledge that leads to increased fund-raising results. And that's the revolution.

About five years ago, I began a quest. I heard a vendor talk about building models for fund raising that would predict donor propensity to give and I wanted that model. I wanted it badly. But I failed to convince our leadership that this was what we needed.

I knew that learning about predictive modeling would help me articulate the need more convincingly. I even had the crazy idea that Bucknell would be best served by having a research staff that knew how to build models in-house. I consider myself a pretty good researcher, but try as I might, I couldn't find a course or a book that would help me. Then one day, I stumbled onto an article in CASE CURRENTS, written by Peter Wylie. Never one for shyness, I called him up. And that was the beginning of a beautiful relationship.

Peter provided our entire research team with user-friendly training in the basics of statistics and predictive modeling. We built a propensity score and tested it with his guidance. We presented this data to our colleagues. Our leadership is excited and the whole development team is throwing ideas at us for the next modeling project. We are officially on our way.

In this book, Peter has managed to capture the simplicity *and* the detail of a basic— and foundation-building—modeling project. Any researcher can pick up this book, work through the steps, and develop a propensity score for their database. It's really that simple. So what are you waiting for? Get started! You'll be amazed at what you can do.

Shelby Radcliff McClintock
Director of Prospect Research and Management
Bucknell University

Acknowledgments

Thanking people for help with a project is not an easy undertaking. The list is always long, and you inevitably leave out someone who shouldn't be excluded.

Nonetheless, I have some folks in mind who deserve special mention:

My data mining students. These are mostly women young enough to be my daughters. For the most part, they work in a university environment. All of them have become vocal proponents for the power of data mining in their institutions. I wrote this book for you gals (and guys, too) who make the work I do so very rewarding.

Bo Schnurr. Bo's a genius. He pointed me in the direction of data mining six years ago, and I haven't looked back since.

The folks at CASE who have encouraged and supported this project and have put up with my (sometimes) impatient, cranky nature.

Robin Netherton, a young woman in the tradition of an old-time editor. Her intelligence and energy and encouragement have made this guide into something I'm very proud of.

Finally, the most important and special person in my world, Linda Ada Margolis, who decided to accept my proposal of marriage almost 30 years ago.

How (and why) to use this guide

I can easily imagine one of your colleagues looking over your shoulder as you read this and saying, "Statistics?! You gotta be kidding me. Doesn't everybody hate that stuff? Isn't that the one course in school we all barely got a 'C' in?"

Sadly, your colleague's comments would be pretty much on the money. Most people who've attended college and grad school have had to take a "stats" course somewhere along the line. And judging from the people I've talked to over the last 30 years, the experience left the vast majority of them with a sour taste in their mouths. They remember dense, expensive textbooks; arcane equations with no apparent practical application; and instructors with poor communication skills. If that was your experience, why would you want to read a guide like this? Statistics in particular, and numerical analysis in general, may be so distasteful to you that nobody (me included) could convince you otherwise.

Even so, most of the people I work with would like to know more than they do about statistics. Why? Because they know that a better grasp of statistics can help them make better use of the vast amount of information in their donor databases.

Let me tell you a story.

A little over a year ago, a medium-sized university contracted me to teach three staff members (over the phone) how to do predictive modeling on their alumni database. They were bright, eager, and excited about the potential of the project. Next thing you know, they had developed a model that used details from their database to generate a score (on a scale from 1 to 30) that ranked a graduate's likelihood of making a major gift. This was great stuff.

But then (as so often is the case with my clients) the project took a back seat to the day-to-day exigencies of fund raising. There were alumni weekends to plan. There were board meetings to prepare for. There were urgent requests from the president's office for information about potential heavy-hitter donors. And on and on. If you work in development, you know what I'm talking about.

But I'm a pesky cuss. I kept after them, saying, "Look, we gotta get these scores into the server for all your alumni. We can't test the model if we don't do that!" They were sympathetic ("We know, Peter, we know"). But I wasn't the one who decided how they spent their time. I was a consultant, not one of their bosses.

Staying just shy of obnoxious, I continued to remind them. Finally, three-quarters of the way through their fiscal year, they had scores for all their alumni entered into the database. I said, "Great, now let's get an output file that lists every graduate, their score, and what they've given so far this fiscal year. This will be a good test of the model, because these scores were never used as part of any campaign. How could they have been? They weren't even in the system!"

Several weeks later we got an Excel file that listed this information. "Okay," they asked, "How should we analyze these data?"

"Tell ya what," I said. "Let's divide the scores into quartiles — the lowest 25% of scores, the next highest 25%, and so on. That'll give us four groups of roughly equal size. Then we'll compute the total amount of dollars that came in from each quartile during the fiscal year."

"That doesn't sound very fancy," they said.

"Exactly," I said. "We're trying to get a message across to vice presidents. We need to keep it simple." I didn't get any argument on that.

This is how the analysis came out:

- Graduates in quartile 1 (the lowest-ranked quartile) gave a total of about $40,000.
- Graduates in quartile 2 gave a little over $200,000.
- Graduates in quartile 3 gave just under $1 million.
- Graduates in quartile 4 (the top-ranked quartile) gave close to $14 million.

Henceforth, there were no more glazed-over eyes and stifled yawns when they talked about data mining to vice presidents and development officers. Nope. Just rapt attention.

So what does this story have to do with statistics?

Well, as you may have guessed, the driving force for this guide is not simply to give people an appreciation for statistics; it's something larger than that. It has to do with the fact that there a lot of smart people in advancement who should be digging into their databases to find out more about their donors and prospective donors. What the field needs is a cadre of in-house professionals who can find the gold residing in their institutional records. Without these professionals doing this kind of digging, we're leaving money on the table. Money that could be going to enormously worthwhile causes.

Here's where statistics come in. The vast majority of young professionals in advancement (who are more than capable of learning how to do data mining) don't have a statistical background. And to do this very important kind of analysis you need some basic statistical knowledge. Not a lot. But enough.

How much do you need to know about statistics?

I've been a student of statistics for more than 35 years. I've taken lots of statistics courses. I've read dozens of books on various aspects of statistics. I did my doctoral dissertation on a statistical topic (one that would put you right to sleep). I've tutored lots of students who were struggling with the topic. And I use statistics just about every day in my work, as I train advancement professionals to do data mining and predictive modeling.

You, on the other hand, are most likely not a statistics expert (or you wouldn't be reading this guide). What's more, you probably don't want—or need—to be one. You need only the essentials, without being burdened with details, terms, and techniques you don't have to know and aren't likely to use. Those essentials are what I hope to give you in this guide: just enough of the basics so that if you want to start analyzing your database with one of the statistical software packages out there, you'll have a clearer sense of what the software can do and how to approach the data.

In writing this guide, I've assumed you work in either annual giving or prospect research, or that you provide support to one or both of these functions.

- If you work in annual giving at a university or a similar institution, your area may be called the "annual fund." At other types of nonprofits, it might well be "membership." While there's certainly a big difference between universities and nonprofits, for the purposes of this guide, those differences aren't all that important. In either type of institution, your focus is mostly on mail and phone campaigns; your prospects include both donors and nondonors; and the specific "ask" is not a huge amount of money. Your primary goal is to maximize participation: You want to hold on to the donors you've already got, and you want to bring in as many new ones as you can. And you want to do all that without wasting lots of money on mail and phone costs.

- If you work in major giving, whether in an educational institution or a nonprofit, you're probably a prospect researcher. Your focus is on identifying individuals who have both the financial resources and the inclination to make a large gift to your cause. Maybe the gift will be in the form of a check; maybe it'll be stocks or land or valuable art pieces; maybe it'll be a bequest. The particular nature of the gift is not so important. What's important is its size.

What do fund-raising professionals—especially those who work in annual giving and prospect research—really need to know about statistics?

- You need to know a little about the concept of **sampling**.

- You need to know a little about **variables**.
- And you need to know about **relationships among variables**. This is where you'll get the most bang for the buck out of statistics.

A practical example

I could talk to you at length about sampling, variables, and relationships among variables. But without some way to tie these concepts into your work, I'd lose you just like those stats professors lost you back in college. For that reason, I'm going to explain these essential elements by showing how they work in practice, as part of a hypothetical project similar to one you might carry out on your own job.

Our sample project will be to build a scoring system for annual fund appeals. (Some people in advancement might call this a "segmentation system.") For the purposes of our example, we'll imagine you work for a medium-sized university somewhere in the Midwest. (We could just as easily have you working for the development office in a large hospital.) We'll assume there is a huge amount of information in your database that will help predict who among your current nondonors is most likely to give in the future.

If we do it right, this sort of scoring system should help us accomplish at least three goals:
- saving money on mailing and phoning costs
- increasing participation in the annual fund
- generating more revenue for annual fund appeals.

Over the course of this guide, we'll walk through an eight-step process to carry out this project. In each step, we'll cover at least one of the three statistical concepts I named above, as follows:

Step 1: Pick some fields in the donor database that we may want to use to build our scoring system (variables, variable relationships).

Step 2: Draw a sample and build a file to analyze (sampling).

Step 3: Import the file into a statistical software package and split it in half (sampling).

Step 4: Take a close look at the variables in the development sample (variables).

Step 5: Look for promising predictors in the development sample (variables, variable relationships).

Step 6: Build an experimental scoring system (variables, variable relationships).

Step 7: Check out the scoring system on the cross-validation sample (sampling, variables, variable relationships).

Step 8: Test the scoring system on a limited appeal (sampling, variables, variable relationships).

One more thing before we get into the project: This guide is not an exhaustive textbook on how to do data mining on fund-raising databases. I wish it were. A book like that definitely needs to be written. Here, though, I'm trying to cover only the bare minimum of what I think you need to know about statistics in your role as an advancement professional.

While I fully understand and empathize with people's feelings about poorly taught classes and badly written texts, I don't want to discourage anyone from going beyond what I cover here. Quite to the contrary, I'd be delighted if you picked up a statistics text and perused it, or took a statistics course taught by someone with a solid reputation as a teacher. In the appendix, I've included some suggestions on approaches to learning more about all this stuff that I find so very fascinating.

For now, I hope you find this guide helpful. More important, I hope you find it helps you and your development colleagues save money and generate more revenue on your various campaigns.

Let's get started.

Pick some fields in the donor database that we may want to use to build our scoring system

Our goal in this project is to build a scoring system that will eventually help us pick out people in your database who are likely to give frequently (and hopefully in large quantity) to the university.

Here's a great place to start talking about one of the three major concepts I want to cover in this guide: variables. Variables are things that people (donors and prospective donors in this case) "vary" on. For example, there is a field in your database called "total amount." This field lists the total dollars each individual—that is, each alumnus, each parent, each friend, etc.—has given the institution since that person's record has been in the database. As you well know, total amount varies enormously from one record to another. Many people (far more than you'd like) have given absolutely nothing. A good portion have given, what, maybe up to a total of $100? And a few (very few) have given huge amounts that go up into the million-dollar-plus range.

Total amount will be a very important variable for us to look at as we build our scoring system. Why? Because we'll be looking for other variables in your database that are related to what people have given the institution.

For example, take the variable "age." You'd expect people in the database who are over 40 to have given more to the institution than people under 40. Of course, there will be plenty of exceptions where specific people under 40 will have given more than specific people over 40. But, as a general rule, we can pretty safely assume that age is related to giving at your institution.

What other variables in your database might be related to giving? While you think about that, let me suggest a few I have found in my experience that are almost always tied in to giving in university databases:

- **Business phone.** People with a business phone listed in the database are more likely to have given than people without a business phone listed.
- **E-mail address.** People with an e-mail address listed in the database are more likely to have given than people without an e-mail address listed.
- **Marital status.** Just about every university database I've worked with has a field for marital status. The field tends to be about 50% to 60% populated (that is, somewhere between 40% and 50% of the records have no marital code listed). What I generally find is that people who have a marital code listed (regardless of what it is) have given more money and more often than those with no code listed at all. Beyond that, I usually find that people who are listed as "married" or "widowed" (as opposed to "single" or "divorced/separated" or no code at all) give the largest amounts and the most frequently.
- **"Greek" membership.** Of course not all institutions have fraternities or sororities. But for those that do, alumni listed in the database as having belonged to a Greek organization give more (on average) and give more often than those who don't have such a listing.
- **Reunion attendance.** A lot of institutions do not record in their donor databases whether alumni have attended reunions and how often. That's not good, because for those institutions that do keep this kind of information, I see a huge difference in giving among people who've attended no reunions, one reunion, or two or more reunions. This relationship between attendance and giving is so pronounced that I often tell my clients, "If you've got a graduate who is under 35 who has already attended two reunions, pay attention to that person. He or she may not have given you a lot of money yet, but the odds are that it'll happen if you're willing to lay on that kind of special treatment you reserve for your huge donors."

By now, you should be getting the idea that there are lots of variables in your donor database—we've only scratched the surface here—and that some of those variables are related to the very important variable of giving.

Now let's get back to our project. For the sake of simplicity, let's say we've talked to our person in IT and have decided we'd like to work with these fields from our database to build our first scoring system:

- **ID:** The unique number that the institution uses to identify each record in its database.
- **TOTAL_AMT:** The total dollars each individual—that is, each graduate, each parent, each friend, etc.—has given the institution since that person's record has been in the database.
- **PREFYR:** The graduating class that the person (if a former student) prefers to be associated with.
- **MAJOR:** The undergraduate major of the person (if a former student).

- **DOB:** The day, month, and year of the person's birth. (When we ask for this, our IT person warns us that this field is far from fully populated. We ask her to include it anyway because sometimes just the presence or absence of data in a field is related to giving.)
- **GENDER:** Whether the person is male or female.
- **MARITAL_STATUS:** Whether the person is listed as "divorced," "married," "single," "surviving spouse," or "unmarried." (Our IT person reminds us that someone who is listed as unmarried could well be married or separated or widowed or whatever. All we know is what is indicated in the field.)
- **NUM_CHILDREN:** The number of children the person has listed in the database. (We have no easy way to determine how accurate or dated this information is.)
- **FRAT:** Whether or not the person (if a former student) belonged to a fraternity or sorority while an undergraduate at the institution. (We don't need to know which fraternity or sorority.)
- **STUD_ORG:** Whether or not the person (if a former student) belonged to at least one student organization while an undergraduate or a graduate student. (Again, we don't need to know which organization.)
- **ZIP:** The ZIP code, if the person lives in the United States. (Our IT person tells us that some records have only the standard five-digit ZIP code while others have the nine-digit "ZIP+4." We tell her that's good, because sometimes people who have the additional code on record are, on average, better givers than those who don't.)
- **HOME_PHONE:** Whether or not the person has a home phone listed in the database. (Our IT person asks us whether we want the full number or just a "Y" if it's listed and an "N" if it's not listed. We say that for this go-round, a simple yes/no indication is fine. Later on we may want to take a look at differences in giving rates by area code.)
- **BUS_PHONE:** Whether or not the person has a business phone listed in the database. (We tell our IT person that, as with HOME_PHONE, all we need is a yes/no indication.)
- **JOB_TITLE:** Whether or not the person has a job title listed in the database. (We don't need to know what the title is.)
- **EMAIL:** Whether or not the person has an e-mail address (either home or business) listed in the database.

Now let's move on to the next step of our project.

Draw a sample and build a file to analyze

Before we carry out this step, let's talk about some of the basics of sampling.

Sampling is a fundamental part of what the field of statistics is all about. The bad news is that the topic of sampling can get pretty complicated, and most of the texts that explain sampling make it seem even more complicated than it really is. The good news is that you don't need to know all that much about sampling for the statistics you'll use as an advancement professional, and certainly not for the kind of project we're taking on here. In fact, I think all you need to know about sampling is:

- why sampling is important, in statistics in general and for the ways you'll be using it in particular
- the two types of sampling methods you're most likely to use
- how you can rely on the use of a large sample size to ensure that your samples will be very accurate representations of the populations you'll draw them from.

Why is sampling important?

Let's say you wanted to do a survey of your alumni to find out how they feel about the quality of their undergraduate experience at your institution. You and some of your colleagues think these attitudes are closely related to giving, and you think doing the survey would be an important first step in testing out your hypothesis.

One of the first questions that will pop up as you contemplate such a project is who you should survey. For example, should you construct a short questionnaire and mail it out to all your living alumni for whom you have "good" addresses? The survey would certainly reach a lot of people. However, your mailing costs will be high, and your return rate will likely be very low. Additionally, the alumni who respond will likely be different in a number of ways from those who don't respond.

Another alternative would be to do a phone survey. With this approach, your response rate would be higher than with a mailed survey, but trying to call all your alumni would be prohibitively expensive.

So what do you do? The solution that all well-established survey research firms adopt is to draw a sample of alumni to contact. These firms have statistical experts who know that a sample can provide an extremely accurate estimate of attitudes (or whatever else is being measured) in the population from which it's drawn. Although these experts have not effectively solved the problem of nonresponse in surveys, they do know that a high response rate from a sample survey of about 1,000 voters can very accurately predict the choices millions and millions of people are likely to make when they go to the polls several weeks later.

And that's why sampling is so important in statistics. It provides an efficient and relatively inexpensive way to measure something you're concerned about in a large population.

Two basic types of sampling methods

If you read an introductory text on sampling, not only will you get confused pretty quickly, you'll also see that there are myriad techniques for sampling available to statisticians. While I'd be delighted if you were to delve into one of these texts, the only two types of samples you need to know about now are **random samples** and **systematic samples**. Let me try to explain these briefly here; later we'll come back to them in more detail as they relate to this project.

- **Random samples.** The concept of randomness is something a lot of people understand intuitively. For example, most of us would say that a five-card poker hand dealt from a well-shuffled deck is dealt at random. Or that the ping-pong balls we see pop up on television for the daily lottery produce a random series of numbers. In both examples we get a sense of unpredictability. That is, no one poker hand nor one lottery number is any more likely to occur than any other. The outcome depends on chance, fate, fortune, luck, or whatever.

    If you connect that feel for randomness to the idea of a random sample, you pretty much understand the concept. A random sample is simply one drawn from a population (whether that population is records in a database or a warehouse full of widgets) where no one unit in the sample has any more likelihood of being drawn than any other unit. That's it. And often your software can do this for you, using a random-number generator.

- **Systematic samples.** A systematic sample is a near-random sample that works particularly well if the population you want to sample from is in the form of a list. Suppose you want to draw a random sample of 10,000 records from a total of about 100,000 in your database. But you don't have software with a random-number generator, which means you don't have an easy way to pick records at random. You can get a pretty close approximation by just starting with the first record listed and telling the computer to pick every 10th record after that. That's a systematic sample.

So, for a systematic sample:

1. You pick the size of the sample you need. (In our example, that was 10,000.)
2. You divide the total number of units in the population list (here, that's 100,000) by the size of the sample you need and call that number K. (In our example, K=10.)
3. Then you pick every Kth item on the list (in this case, every 10th record).

Sample size and accuracy

I want to reassure you that the samples you'll be using in projects like this are going to be very accurate. So let's work through an example that shows how the accuracy of a sample increases with its size.

Imagine you have a database of over a half-million records. (There are plenty of institutions and nonprofits out there that have even bigger ones.) And let's say the gender breakout for that database is exactly half-and-half—that is, 50% men and 50% women. Now you randomly draw five different samples from that database. The first sample consists of 10 records, the second sample has 100 records, the third sample has 1,000 records, the fourth sample has 5,000 records, and the fifth sample has 10,000 records. For each sample, you compute the percentage of women.

Without going into confusing theories and formulas of sampling, here are the ranges those percentages will fall into 95% of the time:

10 records	18.4%–81.6%
100 records	40.0%–60.0%
1,000 records	46.8%–53.2%
5,000 records	48.6%–51.4%
10,000 records	49.0%–51.0%

As you can see (and as you might expect), the larger the sample, the more likely we'll end up with a group that's 50% women or close to it. Drawing a sample of 10 records to represent the entire database would lead to a lot of inaccuracy. It would be very easy to seriously underestimate or overestimate the true percentage of women. We'd be a lot more accurate if we used a sample of 100 records, but we could still miss the true percentage by a pretty wide margin. And this degree of accuracy (or inaccuracy) applies not only to gender or to characteristics that are evenly split, but to any characteristic: The larger our sample, the more likely our sample will represent the nature of the whole population.

Fortunately, in this and similar kinds of projects, we're going to be using samples that are almost always at least 1,000 records (more often at least 5,000 records). With samples of this size, our estimates won't be perfect, but we're not going to miss the mark by much.

What if your database is larger than a half-million? Or smaller? Don't worry. With samples this large, the size of the universe (for instance, a database of 50,000 versus 500,000) doesn't affect the accuracy of the sample estimate very much at all. While a sample of 5,000 will be a slightly better estimator of a database of 50,000 records than it will be for a database of a half-million records, the practical difference between the two is negligible.

But this does point up another issue that is always on my mind when people draw samples from databases: the procedure you use and the care with which you do it. If you're drawing a random sample, did you use a reliable random-number generator so that no one record has any more likelihood of being drawn than any other record? And the same with a systematic sample. If you intend to draw every fourth record in a database, is that in fact what gets done? Or does the programmer simply give you the first 25% of the records in the database listed by unique ID number? Shortcuts like these can have a huge effect on the accuracy of the sample. For instance, if the records are grouped by class year, taking the first quarter of the database would give you only records from certain classes, instead of a sample evenly distributed over all classes.

Drawing our sample

Now we can get back to our project. You'll remember that our job in this second step is to "draw a sample and build a file to analyze." Most of the work here will be done by our IT person (who's very nice, extremely competent, very busy, and definitely someone whose good side we want to stay on). We'll ask her to go into the database and draw a systematic sample of 10,000 records.

Here are the fields she'll include in the Excel file—the ones we picked in Step 1— along with how each field will actually look in Excel for the first nine records.

- **ID:** The unique number that the institution uses to identify each record in its database.

ID
00000037067
00000037069
00000037073
00000037075
00000037077
00000037080
00000047081
00000047085
00000047090

- **TOTAL_AMT:** The total dollars each individual has given the institution since that person's record has been in the database.

TOTAL_AMT
4,565.00
1,284.00
5.00
918.34
595.00
3,490.00
0.00
1,130.00
64,170.00

- **PREFYR:** The graduating class that the person (if a former student) prefers to be associated with. In this case, it seems that the database starts with a large group of records for the class of 1966. That doesn't mean 1966 is the oldest class in the database, just that its ID numbers happen to come first. As long as our sample is drawn evenly from the entire database, the order of the records doesn't make a difference to us.

PREFYR
1966
1966
1966
1966
1966
1966
1966
1966
1966

- **MAJOR:** The undergraduate major of the person (if a former student).

MAJOR
Accounting
Mechanical Engineering
Chemical Engineering
Chemistry
Business Administration
Mathematics
Electrical Engineering
Mechanical Engineering

- **DOB:** The day, month, and year of the person's birth. Here I show the first 14 records (rather than the first nine) because this field is so sparsely populated.

DOB
16-Jan-45
24-Feb-45

- **GENDER:** Whether the person is male or female.

GENDER
M
M
M
M
M
M
M
M
M

- **MARITAL_STATUS:** Whether the person is listed as "divorced," "married," "single," "surviving spouse," or "unmarried."

MARITAL_STATUS
Married
Married
Married
Married
Married
Married
Unmarried
Unmarried
Married

- **NUM_CHILDREN**: The number of children the person has listed in the database.

NUM_CHILDREN
1
2
2
5
3

- **FRAT**: Whether or not the person (if a former student) belonged to a fraternity or sorority while an undergraduate at the institution. Notice that our IT person has only indicated a "Y" (for yes) if the person was definitely listed as having belonged to a fraternity or sorority. A blank means either that the person was not a "Greek" member or that we don't know.

FRAT
Y
Y

- **STUD_ORG:** Whether or not the person (if a former student) belonged to at least one student organization while an undergraduate or a graduate student. A blank means either that the person was not a member or that we don't know.

STUD_ORG
Y
Y
Y
Y

- **ZIP:** The ZIP code, if the person lives in the United States.

ZIP
85718-8904
24450-4610
16046-4645
63141-7308
32460-3407
13760-6728
96962-0881
13486-1725
10934-9740

- **HOME_PHONE:** Whether or not the person has a home phone listed in the database. Notice that she has not indicated an "N" for "no phone listed." That's something we need to ask her about.

HOME_PHONE
Y
Y
Y
Y
Y
Y
Y
Y

- **BUS_PHONE:** Whether or not the person has a business phone listed in the database. Notice that none of the first nine records listed in the Excel file has a business phone listed. It's a good hunch that this is a far more sparsely populated field than HOME_PHONE.

BUS_PHONE

- **JOB_TITLE:** Whether or not the person has a job title listed in the database.

JOB_TITLE
Y
Y
Y
Y
Y
Y
Y
Y

• **EMAIL:** Whether or not the person has an e-mail address listed in the database.

EMAIL
Y
Y
Y
Y

We now have the data on our sample. In the next step, we'll find a way to handle it easily.

Import the file into a statistical software package and split it in half

We now have our Excel file in hand. We could do some analysis right in Excel, but Excel is not great for the kind of exploratory analysis we want to do in this project. So we'll import the file into a statistics package. I happen to like DataDesk. (It's similar to SPSS or SAS, and you can certainly use one of those if that's what you're familiar with. Given the choice, though, I find DataDesk more flexible than either of those packages.)

This is a mechanical process and doesn't have much to do with the substance of statistics—except for one thing. In our university database and in Excel we constantly refer to "fields." Once we've imported the data into DataDesk, we stop using the term "fields" and start saying "variables." Remember, we originally defined variables as things that people (donors and prospective donors in this case) "vary" on. For example, people vary on ID because everyone in our sample has a different ID number. People vary on DOB because they have different dates of birth listed, or they have no date of birth listed. And so on.

Now we have a sample of 10,000 records ready to work with. But we're not going to do our search for predictors of giving with the full sample of 10,000. We're going to split it into random halves, creating two equally random samples of 5,000 records each. The reason for this is that we want to be able to check the results we get in one sample (the development sample) against the results we get in an independent sample (the cross-validation sample).

Let me get a little more specific. One of the hallmarks of good science is the ability to replicate results. In this project, we're actually doing a form of applied science. We've made some assumptions about what may work as predictors of giving, and we'll be testing those assumptions rigorously. Like good scientists, we want to document what we're doing so that someone can come in after us, check our work, and come up with the exact same results we do.

But it's not enough to simply be able to replicate the results on a given sample. You also want to ensure that you haven't—however unintentionally—capitalized on chance. That is, it's easy to take advantage of the idiosyncrasies of one sample to generate a scoring formula/segmentation schema that looks great on that particular sample, but turns out to be not so great on another sample. So we want to hedge our bet. We want to see if the relationship between scores and giving we get in one sample looks as good (or almost as good) on another sample. If it does, then we can be confident we're headed in the right direction. If not ... well, we'll cross that bridge when we come to it.

Understanding Variables

If you're impatient to move on with the step-by-step description of the data mining process, you can skip this section for now. However, at some point you should return to this, because variables are what statistics is ultimately all about, and certainly what data mining and predictive modeling is all about.

Most of the "hard" statistical information you'll find in this guide is concentrated in this section. In the following pages, we'll discuss:

- categorical and quantitative variables
- "hybrid" variables
- different ways to summarize variables.

Categorical and quantitative variables

Although statisticians have never fully agreed on all the different types of variables, for my money there are two primary types: categorical and quantitative.

- **Categorical variables.** These are variables for which it makes no sense to say that one category of data is "more" or "less" than another. For example, take the field "PREFIX" in a database. The "PREFIX" field has categories such as "Mr.," "Ms.," "Mrs.," "Dr.," and so on. We can't say that "Mr." is more than "Ms." or that "Dr." is less than "Mrs." All we can say is that people vary in terms of their prefixes. Other examples of categorical variables are religion, blood type, and hair color.

- **Quantitative variables.** For these variables, it does make sense to say that one category is more or less than another. Age is a quantitative variable because it's measured in years; age 50 is more than age 49. Weight is a quantitative variable, because 175 pounds is more than 174 pounds. Variables measured in dollars are also typically quantitative variables—that is, $1,000 is more than $999.

One good way to decide whether a variable is categorical or quantitative is to ask: "Would it make sense to compute an average (the technical term is 'mean') for this variable?" If the answer is yes, the variable is almost certainly quantitative; otherwise it's almost certainly categorical.

Let's look at a few of the variables in our development sample and decide which are categorical and which are quantitative.

- ID: Remember, this is a unique number that the institution uses to identify each record in its database. On the surface, it looks like a quantitative variable because all the entries are numbers. But if we ask our question—"Would it make sense to compute an average for this variable?"—the answer has to be no, just as it would-n't make sense to compute an average for the numbers on the jerseys of basketball players. These numbers are just a clear way to identify people; they don't imply any sense of "more than" or "less than." So ID is a categorical variable.

- TOTAL_AMT: This field lists the total dollars each individual has given the institution since that person's record has been in the database. Since it clearly would make sense to compute an average for this one, we can be pretty sure that TOTAL_AMT is a quantitative variable.

- MAJOR: This field notes the undergraduate major of the person. It certainly wouldn't make any sense to compute an average for this one. It's clearly a categorical variable.

Hybrid variables

As far as I know, "hybrid variable" is not a term you'll find in any statistical or measurement textbook. It's a term I made up to deal with a problem I often encounter with this kind of project. For example, consider the variable NUM_CHILDREN, which tells us the number of children the person has listed in the database.

NUM_CHILDREN
1
2
2
5
3

Since it would certainly be reasonable to compute an average for this one, is there any reason we shouldn't call it a quantitative variable? Maybe, but what do we do about the blanks? Do we assume any person with no entry for NUM_CHILDREN has no children and just enter a o for that record?

I don't like that solution because we simply don't know what the situation is. All we know is there's nothing listed for the record. So I'm much more inclined to code the blanks as "not listed" or "DK" (don't know). And there's the rub. If I do that, then we have a variable that has both "numeric" and "alpha" data from the standpoint of how the statistical software deals with the variable. That is, if we want to compute an average for NUM_CHILDREN, we can only do it for those records that have a number coded; we can't do it for the records that have a code of "not listed" or "DK."

So we end up with a variable that is both quantitative and categorical—a hybrid variable. These don't get talked about in statistics textbooks, but they're definitely a fact of life in the kind of data analysis work we're doing here.

Ways to summarize categorical, quantitative, and hybrid variables

We've covered two different types of variables and we've talked about my idea of a hybrid variable. Now we can talk about some ways to summarize these variables. But first let's discuss why summarizing variables is a good thing to do.

Consider the variable MARITAL_STATUS, which indicates whether the person is listed as "divorced," "married," "single," "surviving spouse," "unmarried," or "widowed." Here's how the first nine records looked:

MARITAL_STATUS
Married
Married
Married
Married
Married
Married
Unmarried
Unmarried
Married

Imagine looking at this variable as a field in Excel. If we scroll down through the thousands of records in the file, we'll see entries for "divorced," "married," "single," and so on slide by. While it's useful to glance at all this raw data to get a sense of how it's stored, it's very hard to get our arms around all those entries.

But what if we constructed a table like this one that shows the frequencies and percentages of each marital code in our development sample?

Table 1

Marital Status	Count	%
Divorced	8	0.16
Married	2935	58.87
Single	2	0.04
Surviving spouse	1	0.02
Unmarried	2031	40.73
Widowed	9	0.18
Total	**4986**	**100.00**

All of a sudden what was a mass of data becomes a little easier to get some perspective on. At a glance, we can learn a number of facts about our database:

• Almost 60% of the records list "married."

• About 40% list "unmarried."

• The other categories (as a total) constitute less than one-half of 1% of our database.

Those are facts. Nobody can dispute them unless they find an error in our computations. But a summary like this does more than reveal facts. It stimulates interesting questions. For example, in this project we're on a hunt for predictors of giving. So when I look at a table like this, I start asking things like:

"How do the 'marrieds' differ from the 'unmarrieds' in terms of giving? Do the former give more than the latter, or vice versa? Does age affect the difference in giving between these two groups? For example, do young 'marrieds' give less than young 'unmarrieds' because they have less disposable income? But does that pattern change as people get older and their kids leave the nest?"

So summarizing a variable allows us to:

• see the variable more as a *whole* than as a mass of data

• uncover important *facts* about the variable

• raise important *questions* about the relationship of the variable with other variables.

What are some good ways to summarize variables? I think this is an area where most statistics textbooks start confusing students and ultimately turn them off to the whole topic of statistics. For example, if you took a stats course in college or grad school, you undoubtedly had terms like these thrown at you:

• measures of central tendency

• measures of dispersion

• variance

• standard deviation

• interquartile range

• histogram

• frequency polygon.

Each of these terms refers to a way of summarizing variables. And each, if you want to get into statistics in depth, is worth knowing about and studying. (In fact, I find them very interesting and never tire of learning more about them.) But most students I've dealt with start glazing over at the bare mention of these terms.

So exactly how much do you really need to know about summarizing variables, for your purposes? As far as I'm concerned, if you can make a table or chart that shows the percentage distribution of a variable and a vice president can understand it, then you know how to summarize a variable.

I'm only half-joking about the vice president. Truth is, a lot of them tend to be number-phobic or impatient with numbers or both. And the vice president who's going to look over your results wants to understand the point of what you're trying to say, not the details of how you developed your point. So let's say you construct a table or chart that shows a percentage distribution of a variable in your database and show it to a vice president. If he or she looks interested or even intrigued (rather than looking confused or bored), I think you've got it.

Before we move on, let's deal with a delicate subject: percentages. Some people are very comfortable with percentages, and some people aren't. To get any real value out of this guide, you have to be at least reasonably comfortable with percentages. So here's a little test:

1. What is 50% of 300?
2. What is 25% of 200?
3. What is 10% of 1,000?
4. What percentage of 300 is 60?
5. What percentage of 400 is 100?
6. What percentage of 1,000 is 365?

(Answers are at the bottom of the page.)

You shouldn't have had any trouble getting the answers (without using a calculator) in a matter of seconds. If you did have trouble, find a basic math book and brush up, or get a helpful person who's good at numbers to tutor you. And whatever you do, don't get down on yourself because you find percentages confusing. I barely squeaked by introductory calculus in college. Yet I run into several people a month who did well in advanced calculus and struggle with percentages. It's one of the great mysteries of life, and I don't worry about it. Neither should you.

Now let's talk about how to make a percentage distribution for a variable. We'll start with how to do it for categorical variables, because that's pretty easy. Then we'll move on to quantitative and hybrid variables, where making percentage distributions is a little more complicated—but only a little.

1: 150; 2: 50; 3: 100; 4: 20%; 5: 25%; 6: 36.5%.

Making a percentage distribution for a categorical variable

We've already seen an example of a percentage distribution for a categorical variable. Remember this table we made up for MARITAL_STATUS?

Table 1

Marital Status	Count	%
Divorced	8	0.16
Married	2935	58.87
Single	2	0.04
Surviving spouse	1	0.02
Unmarried	2031	40.73
Widowed	9	0.18
Total	**4986**	**100.00**

Actually, this is a table for both a frequency distribution and a percentage distribution. It shows the frequency (that is, the number, or "count") of records that fall into each category of the variable as well as the percentage of records that fall into each category.

Here's how the percentage distribution would look in chart form:

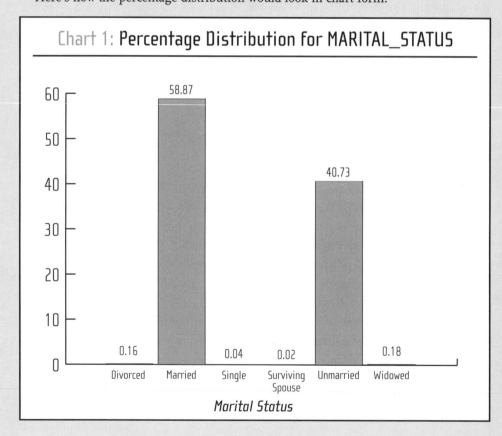

Chart 1: **Percentage Distribution for MARITAL_STATUS**

As you can see, making up a percentage distribution for a categorical variable is pretty straightforward. All you do is ask your software to count up the number of records in each category and convert those numbers to percentages. Then you construct either a table or a chart to display the percentages.

Let's talk a bit about tables and charts. My experience has been that most people (certainly most vice presidents) have a much easier time with charts than they do with tables. The old adage that a picture is worth a thousand words (or numbers, in this case) seems to apply here. So, by all means, use charts to "draw a picture of your data," especially when your goal is to convey information to someone who has neither the time nor the interest (nor possibly the aptitude) to deal with a lot of number detail.

On the other hand, if you're going to be spending much time analyzing data, I'd recommend you get comfortable with tables. Tables are certainly harder to read than charts. But they have at least two distinct advantages over charts:

- **Tables convey more information in less space.** For example, if you compare the table and chart above for MARITAL_STATUS, you'll notice the table contains the frequencies as *well* as the percentages for each of the categories in this variable. If we tried to include both frequencies and percentages in the chart, the chart would get overly "busy" and end up confusing rather than enlightening people.

- **Tables make it easier for others to check and replicate your work.** I'll admit it. I'm a bit uncomfortable with the idea of someone coming in behind me and checking my research work. Despite that discomfort, however, I want my clients and anyone else who reads my work to feel confident I'm painting a full and accurate picture of my analyses. If I just give them a chart like the one above, it's harder for them to see what I've done than if I give them *both* the chart and the table. If they want to take a quick look at the chart and move on, fine. But if they want to see how I arrived at those rather striking percentages displayed in the chart, they can go to the table and look at the frequencies those percentages are based on. They can even raise a question like: "How come there are only 4,986 records listed instead of the 5,000 you said were supposed to be in there, Peter?" Gulp. It turns out that 14 out of the 5,000 records weren't coded. That is, they were left blank—and I should have had yet another category for blanks. A minor detail? Maybe, but it keeps me on my toes.

Making a percentage distribution for a quantitative variable

Earlier I said that making a percentage distribution for a quantitative variable is a little more complicated than making one for a categorical variable. The only reason it's more complicated is that a quantitative variable *usually* has so many categories. To explore this, let's start with a quantitative variable that does *not* have a lot of categories, such as NUM_CHILDREN:

NUM_CHILDREN
1
2
2
5
3

You'll remember that NUM_CHILDREN is a hybrid variable because of all the blank entries. But if you look at the table and the chart below, you can see there are simply not that many categories—nine in total including the blank category. That's not so many categories that we can't get a pretty good "feel" for the variable in a matter of a few seconds. Most records (almost two-thirds) fall in the "blank" category; almost all the rest represent people who have 1–4 kids listed in the database; and fewer than 1.5% of the records have five or more kids listed.

Table 2

# of Children	Count	%
1	423	8.46
2	797	15.94
3	333	6.66
4	121	2.42
5	41	0.82
6	13	0.26
7	2	0.04
8	1	0.02
Blank	3269	65.38
Total	**5000**	**100.00**

In this case, the number of categories is relatively easy to present in a chart:

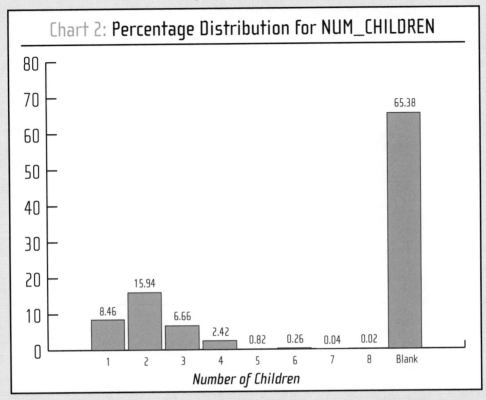

Chart 2: **Percentage Distribution for NUM_CHILDREN**

But what happens when we have a variable such as TOTAL_AMT, which lists the total dollars each individual has given the institution since that person's record has been in the database?

TOTAL_AMT
4,565.00
1,284.00
5.00
918.34
595.00
3,490.00
0.00
1,130.00
64,170.00

Now we've got a problem, because this one has 878 categories, ranging from $0 given to over $1,000,000 given. Obviously we wouldn't consider making a table or chart with well over 800 categories.

So what do we do? One solution would be to divide the variable up into a few chunks that make it easier to get our arms around it. Since about a third (34.76% to be exact) of the records in our development sample have given nothing at all to the university, one thing we could do is divide TOTAL_AMT roughly into thirds—that is, the bottom third, middle third, and top third of givers.

To do that we'll need a little help. One of the nice things about statistical software packages such as DataDesk is that they will quickly display the percentage distribution for a quantitative variable no matter *how* many categories it has.

For example, what you see below is a small, beginning portion of a very long table that Datadesk kicked out for me.

Table 3

$Total Given	Count	Cumulative Count	%	Cumulative %
0	1738	1738	34.76	34.76
1	8	1746	0.16	34.92
2	1	1747	0.02	34.94
3	1	1748	0.02	34.96
5	35	1783	0.70	35.66
6	2	1785	0.04	35.70
9	1	1786	0.02	35.72
10	54	1840	1.08	36.80
11	1	1841	0.02	36.82
14	1	1842	0.02	36.84
15	24	1866	0.48	37.32

Let me explain it:

• The first column, $TOTAL GIVEN, lists the individual total dollar amounts given to the university for all records in this sample.

• The column COUNT lists the number of people in the sample who have given that particular amount. For example, 1,738 people in this sample have given a total of zero dollars; eight people have given a total of $1 (I'm not kidding); one person has given $2; and so on.

• The column CUMULATIVE COUNT lists the total number of people in that sample who have given up to a certain amount. For example, 1,866 people in this sample have given up to $15 (total) to the university.

• The fourth column, labeled "%," lists the percentage of people in this sample who have given a particular amount. For example, the 1,738 people who have given zero dollars constitute 34.76% of the total sample of 5,000 people.

• And, finally, the last column, CUMULATIVE %, lists the total percentage of people in the sample who have given up to a certain amount. For example, 37.32% of the people in this sample have given up to $15 (total) to the university.

We want to divide TOTAL_AMT into thirds. We know the bottom third is going to be people who've given $0 to the university. (Actually, since they constitute 34.76% of the sample, they make up a bit more than a third, but that's fine.)

How about the middle third? Much further down on this long table, DataDesk tells us that 66.84% of the people in this sample have given a total of up to $250. So we know our middle third consists of people who have given more than $0 (that's our bottom third) and less than $251. In other words, our middle third consists of people who have given anywhere from $1 to $250 to the university.

And our top third? That's anyone who's given $251 or more to the university.

Here's how these "thirds" look in table form:

Table 4

Giving Category	Count	%
Bottom third ($0)	1738	34.76
Middle third ($1–$250)	1604	32.08
Top third ($251 or more)	1658	33.16
Total	**5000**	**100.00**

And the following page shows how they look in chart form:

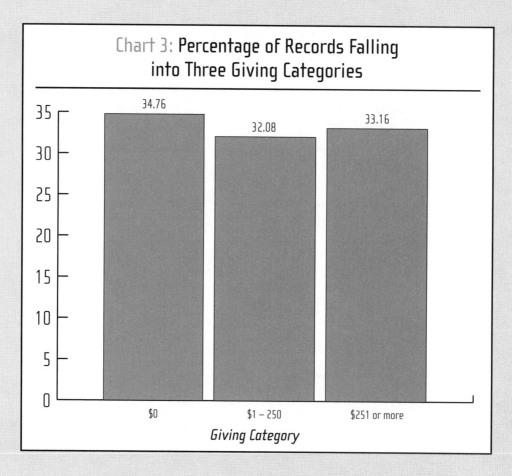

Chart 3: Percentage of Records Falling into Three Giving Categories

34.76 32.08 33.16

$0 $1 – 250 $251 or more

Giving Category

Another way to summarize quantitative variables

I think you know enough right now to adequately summarize any variable—categorical, quantitative, or hybrid. But there are two other measurements we really can't ignore. One is called the "mean," and the other is called the "median." If you've taken any kind of a stats course, you undoubtedly recognize both terms. You may even be asking, "Ah ... what about the 'mode'? Doesn't that belong in there, too?"

Let's dispense with the "mode." It just means the most frequently occurring category in any variable. You see the mode referred to all the time in statistics textbooks, but it rarely (very rarely) gets used in practice.

But the mean and the median do get cited and used a lot with quantitative variables. So let's talk about what each term means, and then let me offer my opinion on the use of both for the kind of practical data analysis we're doing here.

- **The mean.** "Mean" is just the technical term for "average"—a term we hear or read about almost every day. It refers to the sum of values for a variable in a sample divided by the number of objects/records in the sample. For example, let's take the variable TOTAL_AMT for our development sample of 5,000 records. If we add up all the amounts listed in each record, we get a total of $6,922,540. If we divide that amount by 5,000 (the number of records) in the sample, we get an amount of $1,384.51. So the mean (average) total amount that each individual has given is slightly less than $1,400.

- **The median.** The median is the midpoint of a variable—that value of a variable below which 50% of the records fall and above which 50% of the records fall. For our sample here of 5,000 records, the median value is $65. That is, in this sample, half the people have given a total of less than $65, and half have given a total of more than $65.

There's an obvious question here: Why, in this sample, is there such an enormous difference between the mean and the median (about $1,400 versus $65)? The answer is that the mean is very sensitive to extreme values, which can pull it way up or down. The median, on the other hand, is not sensitive to such extreme values.

Let's take a simple example. Say we have two samples of 11 records each:

Sample A

Record	TOTAL_AMT
1	0
2	0
3	50
4	50
5	75
6	100
7	125
8	150
9	150
10	200
11	200

Sample B

Record	TOTAL_AMT
1	0
2	0
3	50
4	50
5	75
6	100
7	125
8	150
9	150
10	200
11	2,000

The only difference between these two samples is that the amount for record #11 in sample A is 200 and the amount for record #11 in sample B is 2,000. Otherwise, the two samples are exactly the same.

If we compute the median for both samples, what value do we get? (Remember the median is the midpoint of a variable—that value below which 50% of the records fall and above which 50% of the records fall.) It's 100, because in both samples five records fall below 100 and five records fall above 100.

But what about the means for the two samples? If we add up all the amounts for each record in sample A, we get 1,100; dividing that amount by 11, we get a mean of 100. But if we do the same arithmetic for sample B? We get a total of 2,900 and a mean of 263.64. Why? That one record (#11) in sample B makes all the difference. While that record has no effect on the median, it "pulls" the mean up quite a bit.

Using both the mean and the median to summarize quantitative variables

In the appendix (pages 77–79), I've named a couple of statistical texts that go into some detail on the advantages of using both these measures of what is technically referred to as "central tendency." Those details are definitely worth reading about if you have the time and inclination.

But here all I have to say about the mean and the median is this: *use both of them.* All statistical software packages provide both these measures (as well as a host of others) to describe and summarize quantitative variables. So take advantage of that. If the mean and median for a certain variable are very different (as with the pair of examples above), pay particular attention to that, because that difference means there are some very big (or possibly) very small values "pulling" or "dragging" the mean up or down.

Take a close look at the variables in the development sample

In the section "Understanding Variables" (pages 23–36), you'll find some detailed background information about variables and how to summarize them. On your first reading of this guide, it's OK to skip that section. Eventually, though, you'll find that material useful as you do your own data mining and predictive modeling.

For now, let's continue with our project to build a scoring system for annual fund appeals. Early on we said our goal for this project is to create a tool that will help us pick out people in your database who are likely to give frequently and generously to the university. To do that, we're going to identify "predictors"—that is, we're going to find variables in your database that are related to overall giving.

This is a hypothetical project; we're using it as a practical example to help you learn some basic statistics. If it were an actual project, I would insist you painstakingly go through each of a host of possible predictors and summarize them using the methods I've described in the background section on variables. I think doing that is a very important part of data mining. The trouble is, if we took the time to do that here, you'd get bored and possibly never get through the rest of this guide. That, of course, would not be good.

So let's compromise. Let's take a careful look at one possible predictor we haven't examined yet. We'll summarize it a couple of ways, and we'll also give ourselves a sneak preview of the next step.

Looking closely at preferred graduating class

Earlier we mentioned a variable called PREFYR, which designates the graduating class that the person prefers to be associated with. If we take a look at this variable in DataDesk, we find that 67 different class years are listed in our development sample. The earliest is 1923, with one alumnus listed; the latest is 2000, with 210 alumni listed. (Some years in between are not listed, because people have died or no longer have a good address available; the class years may be represented in the total database, but none of those members made it into the sample.)

So, how do we summarize this set of data to get a clearer picture of all of it?

We have some options. Since PREFYR is a quantitative variable, similar to age, we can compute a mean and a median. (For more detail about quantitative variables, see page 29.) The mean (average) is 1980, and the median (the category below which and above which half the records fall) is 1982. Those two are pretty close. This tells us that no extreme values are pulling the mean up or down.

It's interesting to know that our database of alumni is roughly evenly split between people who graduated before the early '80s and those who graduated after the early '80s. But that doesn't tell us a whole lot. So another option is to make a percentage distribution by decades.

Table 5 shows us the distribution of alumni by class decade, in both frequency and percentages:

Table 5

Class Decade	Count	%
1920s	2	0.04
1930s	17	0.34
1940s	142	2.84
1950s	443	8.86
1960s	502	10.04
1970s	904	18.08
1980s	1507	30.14
1990s	1273	25.46
2000+	210	4.20
Total	5000	100.00

And here's the percentage distribution in chart form:

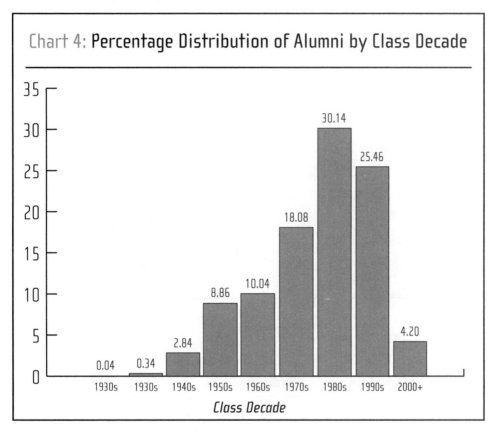

Chart 4: **Percentage Distribution of Alumni by Class Decade**

Interesting, huh? But decades is only one way to "chop up" graduating class years. What if we were to divide up these data into quartiles —that is, the oldest 25%, the next oldest 25%, and so on? Here's how that would look in table form:

Table 6

Class Year Quartiles	Count	%
1972 and earlier	1243	24.86
1973–1982	1309	26.18
1983–1990	1091	21.82
1991 and later	1357	27.14
TOTAL	**5000**	**100.00**

And here's how it would look in chart form:

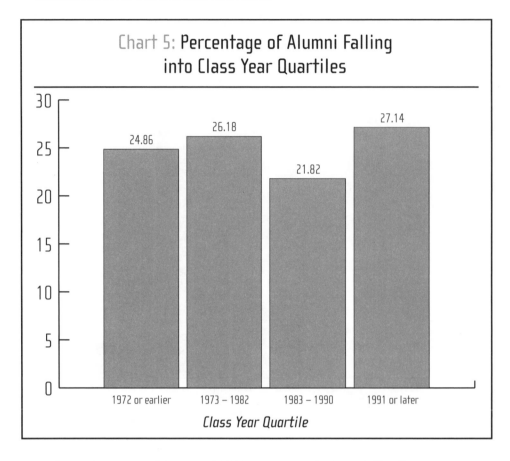

Chart 5: Percentage of Alumni Falling into Class Year Quartiles

In the section on variables, I explain that summarizing a variable allows us to:
- see the variable more as a *whole* than as a mass of data
- uncover important *facts* about the variable
- raise important *questions* about the relationship of the variable with other variables.

Certainly these two tables and charts allow us to see the variable as a whole. But what important facts have we uncovered about the variable? Two points jump right out at me:
- A good half of the alumni are in their early 40s or younger. That's a guesstimate, of course, because we don't have the actual ages of these folks, and some may have attended college at an older age than typical for undergraduates. But if we assume that the year is now 2003 and that most of them graduated at age 22 ... well, you can do the math.
- Applying the same kind of math to the group that graduated in 1972 or earlier, we can see that a good quarter of the alumni are in their early 50s or older.

There are certainly other facts we could point to here, but let's move on to questions about the relationship of preferred graduating class to other variables—in particular, giving. We can pretty safely assume that people who have been out of school a long while have given more than people who've been out only a short while. But how big is that difference? That is, how much more have the older grads given than the other grads?

We're supposed to wait till the next step to answer questions like this, but we'll jump ahead for just a moment. Specifically, let's look at the total dollars contributed by the four quartiles.

Here it is in table form:

Table 7

Class Year Quartiles	Total $ Given
1972 and earlier	$4,712,270
1973–1982	$908,502
1983–1990	$225,317
1991 and later	$65,055

Here it is in chart form:

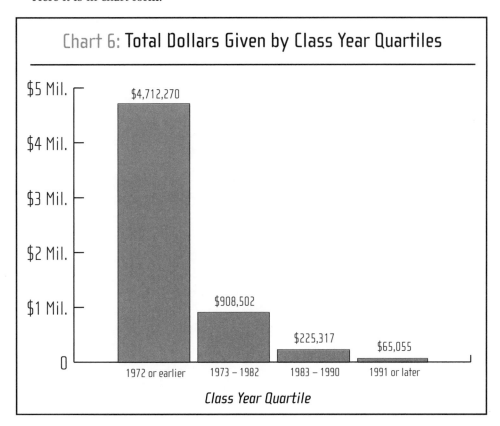

Chart 6: Total Dollars Given by Class Year Quartiles

It should be pretty clear just from looking at this that graduating class is related to giving levels. There are some other ways (admittedly less dramatic than this one) to look at the relationship between graduating class and giving. We'll get into those later on. But I wanted to show you this much now to offer you a little encouragement as you continue through the guide.

Here's my point: If the application of statistics can uncover information like what you see in the chart and table above—information that can eventually save your institution money and help generate a lot more revenue—it seems to me it's worth the effort of trying to apply it. Let's keep going.

Look for promising predictors in the development sample

Ever since I first got interested in statistics, I've been fascinated by the relationships between variables. How humidity level is related to discomfort in the summer. The difference between New Englanders and people from the Southeastern United States on the variable of "chattiness." How the different cultural backgrounds of my wife Linda and me so clearly relate to how we deal with situations that pop up almost every day of our lives.

Professionally, I continue to be fascinated by the relationships I see between certain variables in an institution's donor database and how those variables are so often related (sometimes *highly* related) to giving.

In this section, we're going to get into those kinds of relationships. Specifically, we'll look at the relationships between giving and three of the variables (EMAIL, NUM_CHILDREN, and FRAT). In the process, we'll do these things:

- clarify what is meant by a **predictor** variable and an **outcome** variable
- go over two ways to look at the relationship between these variables and giving— one in which we treat giving as a **categorical** variable, and one in which we treat it as a **quantitative** variable
- consider what "significance" means from a practical as well as statistical standpoint
- talk about causality versus prediction and something I like to call "proxy variables."

Predictor variables and outcome variables

In research in the social and behavioral sciences, it's common to divide variables into two types, indicated with the notations "Y" and "X." The Y variables are frequently referred to as the "outcome" variables. The X variables are frequently referred to as the "predictor" variables. The following explanation should help clarify the difference:

- **Y variables (outcome variables) are variables that researchers try to predict or influence.** For example, in this project, we are ultimately trying to predict the giving behavior of people we will be soliciting in the future. So giving behavior is our outcome variable. If we were doing a laboratory experiment to determine how audience smiling influences the stiffness of a speaker's posture during a speech, our outcome variable would be stiffness of posture.

- **X variables (predictor variables) are variables that researchers use to predict or influence a result.** In our project, these are the many variables, such as graduating class year or marital status, that might enable us to predict the outcome variable of giving behavior. In the laboratory experiment we just described, the predictor variable would be audience smiling.

(If you've had a stats class, you might have heard the Y variable called the "dependent" variable and the X variable called the "independent" variable. These terms make sense in the context of a lab experiment, where you're looking at causes and results, but they don't really apply to the sort of work we're doing now, in which we're only looking for relationships. So don't worry about them here.)

To look at the relationship between each of three predictor variables and our outcome variable of giving, we'll use two different methods: one where we treat giving as a *categorical* variable, and one where we treat it as a *quantitative* variable. (In the "Understanding Variables" section, I go into some detail about the difference between categorical and quantitative variables. For purposes of this step, what you need to know is that quantitative variables involve data that can be ranked as greater or lesser on a measure of quantity, while categorical variables involve data that fall into categories that don't lie on a quantitative scale.) To examine giving as a categorical variable, we'll use a statistical tool usually called a cross-tabulation or contingency table. To examine it as a quantitative variable, we'll compare means and medians. If you're like most of the folks I work with, the second approach will be easier for you to get comfortable with.

Using cross-tabulation to look at the relationship between giving and a possible predictor

A cross-tabulation, or "cross-tab," is a quick way to look at the relationship between two categorical variables, where one variable is designated the outcome (Y) and the other variable is designated the predictor (X). (Remember, in this project our outcome variable will always be giving.)

Let's start with the outcome (Y) variable. Table 4 and Chart 3 (both repeated here from the "Understanding Variables" section) show our sample population divided roughly into thirds based on total amount of giving. We've used a division of three because the people at the lowest level of giving—those who have never given at all—constitute about a third of our sample population. Among the others, the break point at which the subgroups are roughly even lies around $250, so that's where we've broken up our second and third categories. (For more detail on this process, see page 34.)

Table 4

Giving Category	Count	%
Bottom third ($0)	1738	34.76
Middle third ($1–$250)	1604	32.08
Top third ($251 or more)	1658	33.16
Total	**5000**	**100.00**

Now let's take a look at one of the three predictor variables we'll be using in this step:

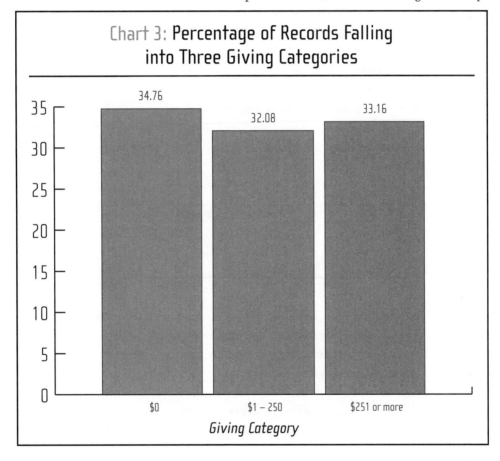

EMAIL. In Table 8, you'll see that a little more than one-third (slightly over 36%) of our sample individuals have an e-mail address listed in the database. The rest (almost 64%) do not have an e-mail address listed.

Table 8

E-Mail Listing	Count	%
No e-mail listed	3178	63.56
E-mail listed	1822	36.44
Total	**5000**	**100.00**

Here's where we can look at the relationship between having an e-mail address and giving. More specifically, we can ask the question: Is there a difference in giving behavior between people with a listed e-mail address versus people without a listed e-mail address?

To begin to answer this question, we make a table like the one you see below. This is a cross-tabulation or contingency table. If you're not used to poring over data summaries, the table may look a bit confusing at first. But if you take your time, you can see it's pretty logically laid out. It lines up the categories from our giving breakdown (down the left edge of the table) against the categories from our e-mail breakdown (across the top of the table) to create all possible combinations—six, in this case—and tells us the number of people in the sample who fall into each of those groups. There are 523 people who have an e-mail listed and have given nothing; 1,215 who don't have an e-mail listed and have given nothing; 594 who have an e-mail listed and have given between $1 and $250; and so on.

Table 9

	No E-Mail Listed	E-Mail Listed	Total
$0	1215	523	1738
$1–$250	1010	594	1604
$251 or more	953	705	1658
Total **3178**		**1822**	**5000**

The problem with this table, however, is it's hard to see from these counts what relationship (if any) there is between having an e-mail address and giving.

But what if we convert these counts to percentages? Let's consider that the 1,822 records in the sample that list an e-mail address constitute 100% of that group. The 3,178 records in the sample that do not list an e-mail address constitute 100% of that group. Does that make it any easier to see if there's a relationship between having a listed e-mail address and giving? Take a look at Table 10 and Chart 7, and see what you think.

Table 10

	No E-Mail Listed	E-Mail Listed	Total
$0	38.2%	28.7%	34.8%
$1–$250	31.8%	32.6%	32.1%
$251 or More	30.0%	38.7%	33.2%
Total	**100.0%**	**100.0%**	**100.1%**

Because of rounding, not all columns add to exactly 100.

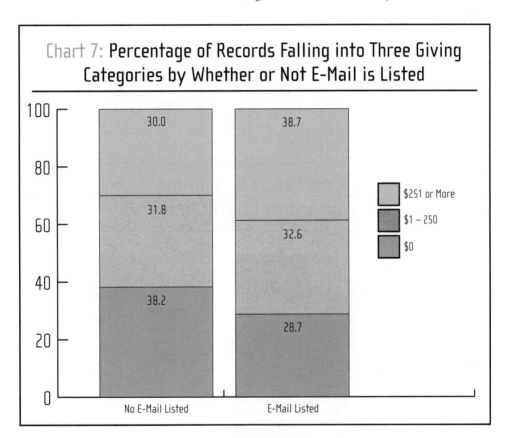

Chart 7: **Percentage of Records Falling into Three Giving Categories by Whether or Not E-Mail is Listed**

Here's what stands out for me:

- If I look at the $0 category, I see that about 29% of the people with an e-mail address have given nothing. But among the people without an e-mail address, 38% of them have given nothing. That's a sizable difference.
- If I look at the middle category of giving ($1–$250), I see that the percentages for those who have an e-mail address and those who don't are nearly identical.
- If I look at the top level of giving ($250 or more), I see that almost 39% of those with an e-mail address fall in this category, compared with only 30% without an e-mail address—another sizable difference.

So far, I have to conclude that people with an e-mail address in the database are less likely to be nondonors and more likely to be large givers than those people without an e-mail address in the database.

Using means and medians to look at the relationship between giving and a possible predictor

Now let's look at the relationship between giving and having an e-mail address when we treat giving as a quantitative variable—that is, a variable where it's appropriate to compute a mean and a median. That information appears in Table 11 and Chart 8.

Table 11

	Count	Mean	Median
No e-mail listed	3178	$1,320.06	$50
E-mail listed	1822	$1,496.91	$110

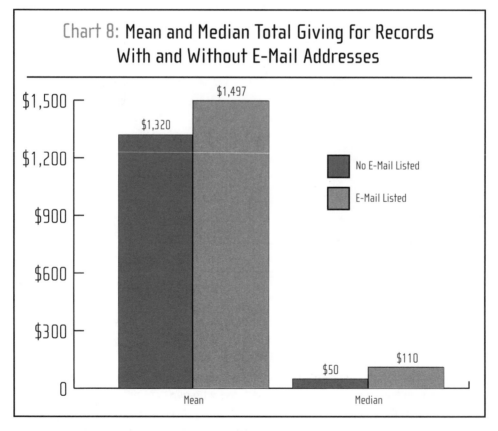

Chart 8: Mean and Median Total Giving for Records With and Without E-Mail Addresses

Here's what I see when I look at this table and chart:

• There's a whopping difference between the mean and the median of total dollars given in both groups—people with an e-mail address listed and those without an address listed. This tells us that a few large donors are "dragging" the mean values upward in each group. (For details, see page 34.)

- There's not much relative difference between the mean total dollars given for people with e-mail addresses and without addresses—about $1,500 versus slightly more than $1,300. There is, however, quite a large relative difference between the medians, $110 versus $50.

It's the difference between these median values that I'm most inclined to pay attention to. Remember the median is the "halfway" point in a distribution; it's the value above and below which 50% of the people in a particular group fall. So I know that for the group with e-mail listed, the halfway point is $110; for the group without e-mail listed the halfway point is $50. I think that's a pretty big difference.

Statistical significance and practical significance

We've now taken two different views of the relationship between having an e-mail address and giving: one where we treat giving as a categorical variable, and one where we treat it as a quantitative variable. From both vantage points, it looks like having an e-mail address in the database may be a good predictor of giving and should eventually be included in our scoring system.

At this point you may be asking some questions I hear pretty often. For example:

- "You talk about a 'sizable' difference. How do you decide what is sizable and what is not? Is there some rule of thumb we can use?"

- "What about statistical significance? I heard a lot about that in the stats course I took. You haven't made any mention of that."

Those are good questions. When I was formulating my thoughts for this guide, I wrestled hard with whether or not to cover a number of concepts that you almost always see in introductory textbooks on statistics. One of those topics is statistical significance, including tests of differences between means (for quantitative variables) and the chi square test of independence (for categorical variables). I decided to leave these topics out for several reasons.

To begin with, several decades' worth of explaining statistical concepts have taught me that the notion of statistical significance confuses an awful lot of people. At times it still confuses me. I don't think you have to understand statistical significance to do the kind of data analysis we're doing in this guide. *But* (and this is a pretty big "but"), I strongly encourage you to explore the concept in some of the references I list in the appendix (pages 77–79). These books explain it better than I could; I think they're worth looking at.

Furthermore, in the examples we're using in this guide (and in the work you're likely to do), the samples are very large—in the thousands of records. With samples this big, even small differences can turn out to be statistically significant when you do a statistical test on them. And that's nice, but what we're looking for here is not statistical significance. We're looking for *practical* significance. We're looking for differences that will have an ultimate effect on your advancement bottom line.

I'm a firm believer that, with practical differences, you don't need a statistical test to confirm what your eyes are already telling you. Take the example we just worked through where we were looking at the relationship between having an e-mail address and giving. As it turns out, the differences in giving between people with and without an e-mail address are *highly* significant from a purely statistical standpoint. But I already knew that as soon as I looked at the percentages in the cross-tab/contingency table.

I still haven't answered your question about a rule of thumb—a guideline for deciding whether or not a difference is practically significant. Here's my rule of thumb. When I look at cross-tab percentages and differences between means and medians, I find that a difference is of practical significance if I say to myself: "Whoa! Look at that!" If I don't have that kind of strong reaction, then the difference is not practically significant for me. That's not a particularly precise nor scientific rule of thumb, but it's stood me in good stead for many years.

Now let's get back to looking at our predictors. We just examined EMAIL; we're also going to look at NUM_CHILDREN and FRAT.

Applying our tools to two more predictors

We'll start with NUM_CHILDREN. Table 2 (repeated here from the "Understanding Variables" section) shows the number and percentage of records listed for each of nine categories: 1–8 children listed and blank (meaning there was no entry for this field for those records in the database; that might mean the person has no children, or just that the university has no record of how many). Chart 2 (also repeated from the previous discussion) shows just the percentage of records for each of the nine categories.

Table 2

# of Children	Count	%
1	423	8.46
2	797	15.94
3	333	6.66
4	121	2.42
5	41	0.82
6	13	0.26
7	2	0.04
8	1	0.02
Blank	3269	65.38
Total	5000	100.00

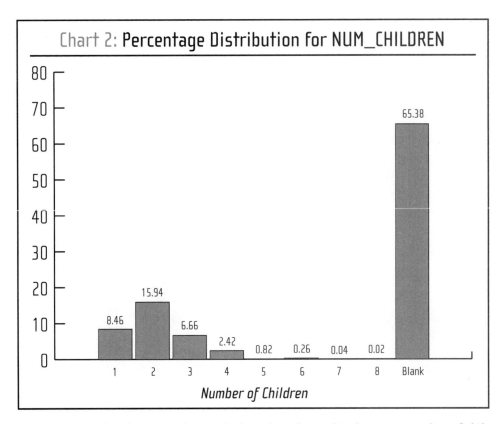

Chart 2: Percentage Distribution for NUM_CHILDREN

Number of Children

Now we need to figure out how to look at the relationship between number of children and giving. Using the figures generated from a cross-tab, we could construct a chart like the one you see on the following page. If you ponder it a while, you can see that there definitely *is* a relationship between number of children listed and giving. And, to tell the truth, I actually like this chart. But from the standpoint of making it clear to someone other than you and me (someone like a vice president), I *don't* like it. It's too "busy." It conveys too much information; we run the risk of confusing rather than enlightening whomever we show it to.

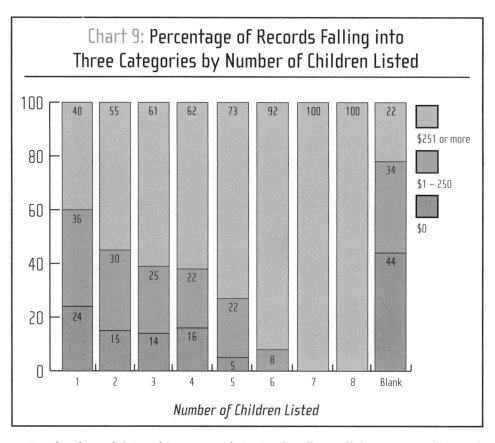

Chart 9: Percentage of Records Falling into
Three Categories by Number of Children Listed

Number of Children Listed

So, what do we do? One thing we can do is simply collapse all the categories from 1–8 into one category and label it "children listed." If we do that, we end up with 1,731 records that list children (about 35% of the sample) and 3,269 records (about 65% of the sample) for which this field is blank. Then we can construct the chart you see on the following page:

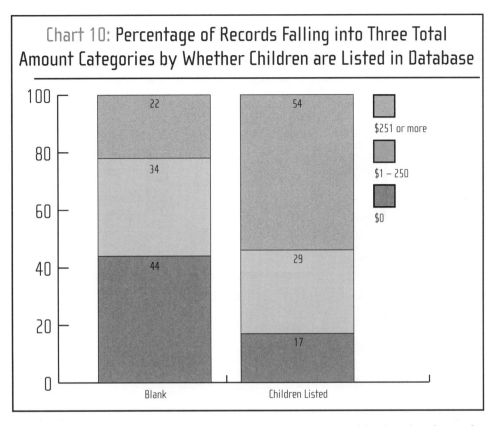

Chart 10: Percentage of Records Falling into Three Total Amount Categories by Whether Children are Listed in Database

Legend:
- $251 or more
- $1 – 250
- $0

Blank: 22, 34, 44
Children Listed: 54, 29, 17

Even though I like the more detailed chart for you and me, I like this chart better for vice presidents and others who aren't digging and foraging in the database the way we are. This chart speaks volumes: It says loud and clear—whoa, look at that!—that people who have at least one child listed in the database are *far* more likely than people without any kids listed to be in the upper third of donors (54% versus 22%) and much less likely to be nondonors (17% versus 44%). What we've done here, of course, is to look at the relationship between having children listed in the database and giving, where giving is a categorical variable.

Chart 11 takes the other approach—it looks at the relationship between having children listed and giving, where giving is a quantitative variable. For that, we look at means and medians. I think this chart tells the same basic story as the last one. Just as with our analysis of e-mail address, what particularly stands out for me here is the difference between the median values for the two groups. Remember the median is the "halfway" point in a distribution; it's the value above and below which 50% of the people in a particular group fall. So I know that for the group with kids listed, the halfway point is $305; for the group without kids listed the halfway point is $25. I think that's a very big difference.

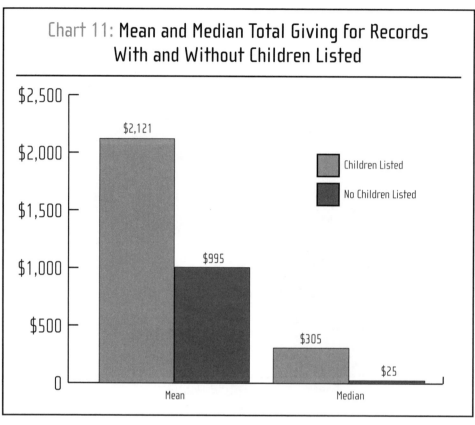

Chart 11: Mean and Median Total Giving for Records With and Without Children Listed

Legend: Children Listed / No Children Listed

Mean: $2,121 (Children Listed), $995 (No Children Listed)
Median: $305 (Children Listed), $25 (No Children Listed)

We'll look at one more predictor in this step: FRAT. The table below shows that about 30% of the people in our database belonged to a fraternity or sorority when they were undergraduates.

Table 12

Fraternity or Sorority	Count	%
Not a member	3467	69.34
Member	1533	30.66
Total	**5000**	**100.00**

By now you're getting the hang of looking at the relationship between two variables. Before you look at the charts that follow, think a little about what you would do in the way of computations to determine whether belonging to a fraternity or sorority is a good predictor of giving. After you do that, look at the charts.

Then, here's what I'd like you to do. Sit down with a colleague or friend who might be at least mildly intrigued by the topic of this guide and describe what we're up to in this project. Then show the person the two charts and explain why you see a strong relationship between belonging to a fraternity or sorority and giving. There's nothing like explaining this stuff to another person to lock the concepts into your brain. It's like explaining the meaning of a big word to a youngster. The effort not only expands the child's understanding of the word; it also expands your own understanding.

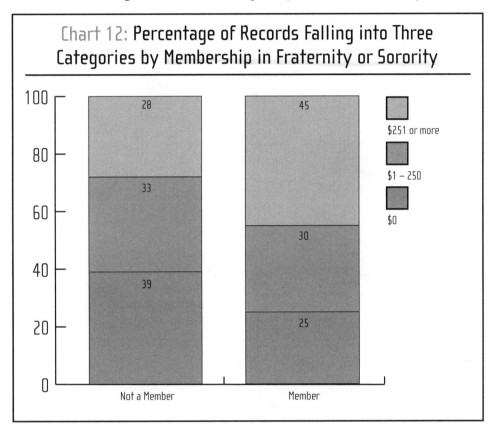

Chart 12: Percentage of Records Falling into Three Categories by Membership in Fraternity or Sorority

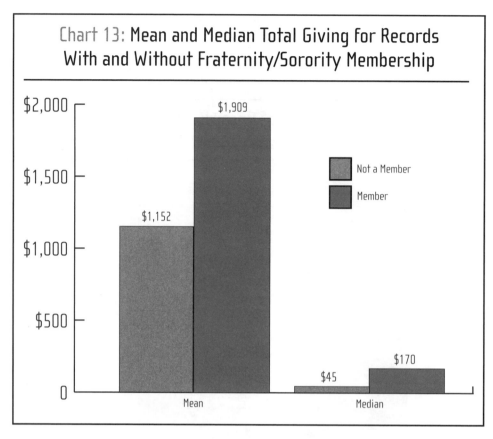

Chart 13: Mean and Median Total Giving for Records With and Without Fraternity/Sorority Membership

Legend:
- Not a Member
- Member

Mean: $1,152 (Not a Member), $1,909 (Member)
Median: $45 (Not a Member), $170 (Member)

Not all predictors are useful

Of the three variables we've looked at, we've had three successes—that is, all three showed a noticeable relationship to giving. Of course, I got to choose the three variables I'd use to walk you through this step, so I picked ones that would show you what to watch for. When you do your own project, your luck probably won't be quite this good. So, how will you recognize when a predictor doesn't relate to giving?

For comparison, let's take a look at a predictor that *won't* prove useful and talk about why not. We'll use a variable I haven't mentioned yet: state of residence. More specifically, we'll look at the relationship between total giving and whether alumni live in the same state as the university or out-of-state. Take a look at charts 14 and 15.

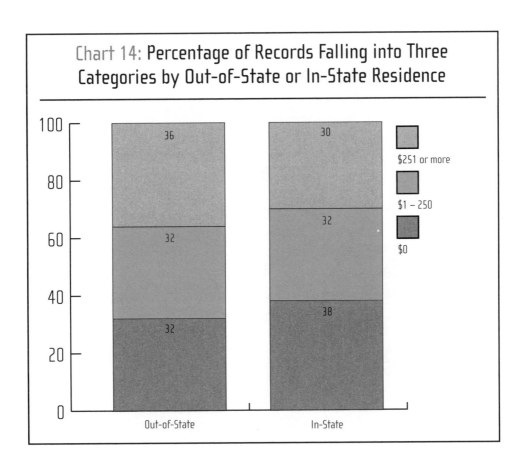

Chart 14: Percentage of Records Falling into Three Categories by Out-of-State or In-State Residence

$251 or more

$1 – 250

$0

Out-of-State

In-State

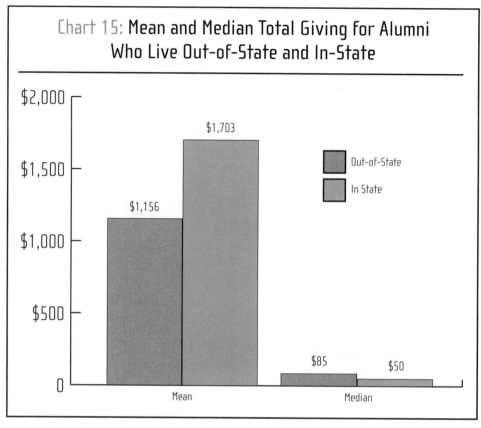

Chart 15: Mean and Median Total Giving for Alumni Who Live Out-of-State and In-State

Based on these charts, here's why I don't think this variable works well as a predictor for our database:

- First and foremost, it doesn't pass the "Whoa, look at that!" test. That is, we don't see striking differences between in-staters and out-of-staters when it comes to total giving, regardless of whether we look at percentage differences or means and medians.

- Almost as important, however, is the fact that the differences we see between the two groups change depending on how we look at those differences. For example, on one hand, the percentage differences in Chart 14 indicate that people who live out-of-state are slightly better givers than those who live in-state. On the other hand, when we look at mean (not median) differences, the in-staters look like better givers than the out-of-staters. This lack of "corroborative testimony" is enough to cause me to dump this one as a possible predictor.

Causality versus prediction and proxy variables

Before we move on to the next step, I'd like to talk briefly about some issues that invariably crop up when I do seminars on data mining for advancement officers. One issue has to do with the difference between causality and prediction. The other has to do with something I call proxy or surrogate variables.

The distinction between causality and prediction crops up in almost all courses in science, and I think it bears repeating here too. In this project we're looking at predictors of giving (e.g., whether or not an e-mail is listed in the database, whether or not kids are listed, and whether someone was a member of a fraternity or sorority). But these variables don't cause people to give or not give. They're not like bacteria that cause colds and disease, nor water in a gas tank that can *cause* an engine to sputter and stall. These variables are simply *related* to giving.

Predictor variables may be related to giving for any number of reasons. For example, an e-mail listing in a university database may be more likely to exist for people who keep in touch with their alma mater, perhaps by filling out forms and surveys that ask for an e-mail address. And people who keep in touch with their institutions may also be more likely to give to their institutions than people who don't keep in touch. We don't know; all we know is that people with e-mails listed are more likely to be donors than those without e-mails listed. Again, having an e-mail address doesn't cause giving, but from a statistical point of view, it predicts (is related to) giving.

Sometimes, though, a variable appears to be a predictor when in fact it's simply another measure of giving. I call this a proxy variable.

Let's use an example. Say your institution has something called the "Silver Club," which is reserved for alumni who have given the institution a lifetime total of $1,000 or more. And let's say there's a field in your database that's called SILVERCLUB, coded "Y" if you're a member and "N" if you're not a member. We wouldn't want to use SILVERCLUB as a predictor because it's a proxy variable. That is, it's a "proxy" for giving. The only way you can belong to the Silver Club is by having given (quite a bit) to the institution.

"But hold on," you say, "What about things like e-mail and business phone listings in our database. Don't we get those from people who've given money? So aren't they proxy variables, too?" Yes, sometimes you get that information when people make a gift, but it's not the only way you get it. The reason you know that something like e-mail or business phone is not a proxy variable is that there are plenty of people in your database with an e-mail listed or a business phone listed who haven't given you a penny. That's not the case with something like the Silver Club. The only way you can be in the Silver Club is by having given.

On to the next step.

Build an experimental scoring system

So far we've identified three promising predictors of giving at our institution:
- whether or not someone has an e-mail listed in the database
- whether or not someone has children (regardless of how many) listed in the database
- whether or not someone is listed in the database as having belonged to a fraternity or sorority.

Of course, in an actual data mining and predictive modeling project, we would want to go on and identify a lot more predictors. But for our purposes now, we've got enough to move to the next step in the process: building an experimental scoring system.

It's easy to make this step complicated, but let's save the complications for later. For now, all we have to do is two things:

1. make each of our predictors into a 1/0 variable
2. add those 1/0 variables together to make a total score for each record that can range from 0 to 3.

A 1/0 variable is simply a numeric (as opposed to an alpha) variable that has two categories, which we label as 1 and 0. That allows us to add variables together, something we can't do for data recorded as words or letters.

For the three predictors we've been working with, creating 1/0 variables is simple enough because we've already reduced each of them to two categories—"yes" and "no":
- Yes, someone has an e-mail listed in the database; no, someone does not have an e-mail listed in the database.
- Yes, someone has children listed in the database; no, someone does not have children listed in the database.

• Yes, someone is listed in the database as having belonged to a fraternity or sorority; no, someone is not listed as having belonged to a fraternity or sorority.

To convert each of these variables to 1/0 form is simply a matter of telling our software to make every "yes" a 1 and every "no" a 0. Bear in mind you will not always want a "yes" in the database to match up to 1. For all three examples here, it happens that a "yes" answer relates to greater giving. For some other predictors, you might find that a "no" answer corresponds with greater giving. If so, then you would count "no" as 1 and "yes" as 0. Similarly, if one of our predictors were "gender" and our analysis showed that men gave more than women, we would assign a 1 to "male" and a 0 to "female," but if women gave more than men, we'd assign a 1 to "female" and a 0 to "male."

Once we have these numeric values, we can add the variables for each record together to get a score. When we add up all the 1s and 0s for our three 1/0 variables, we get a score of 0, 1, 2, or 3 for each record. Here's the frequency and percentage distribution of scores we end up with for this sample:

Table 13

Score	Count	%
0	1709	34
1	1834	37
2	1119	22
3	338	7
Total	**5000**	**100**

Notice that 1,709 of our records (about a third of them) got a score of 0. That means that each one of these records did not have an e-mail address listed, did not have any children listed, and did not list membership in a fraternity or sorority.

What about the 1,834 records that got a score of 1? That means each of them had one of these three items listed, but not the other two. A record in this category might have had e-mail listed but no kids and no fraternity or sorority; a fraternity or sorority, but no e-mail nor kids; one or more kids, but no e-mail nor fraternity or sorority. Other combinations can lead to a score of 2. A score of 3, of course, means the record had a "yes" for all three variables.

Charts 16 and 17 show the relationship between these scores and giving. I won't go into the details of what these charts contain. You can see and interpret those for yourself.

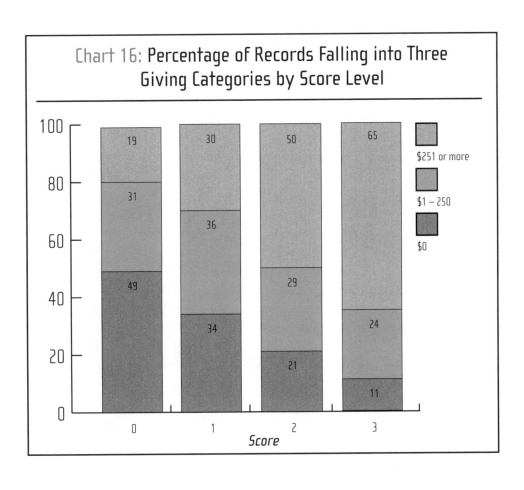

Chart 16: Percentage of Records Falling into Three Giving Categories by Score Level

$251 or more

$1 – 250

$0

Score

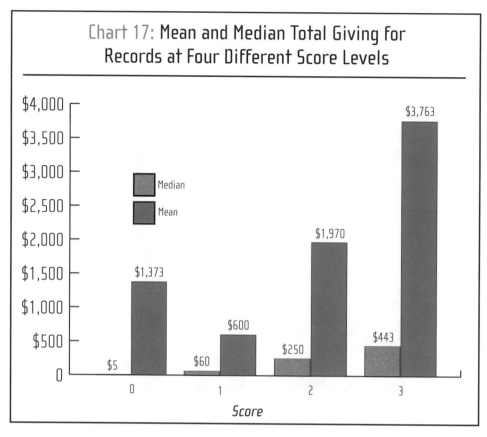

Chart 17: Mean and Median Total Giving for Records at Four Different Score Levels

Converting more complicated variables to a 1/0 form

These particular variables—e-mail address, children, and fraternity/sorority member-ship—translated smoothly to a 1/0 format. Not all variables are quite so easy to handle, but with a little ingenuity, you can generally find ways to boil more complex variables down into a form you can use for scoring.

In general, you should start by looking for one or two data groups within the variable that contain at least 10% of the total records in the sample and that stand out from the rest of the data categories for that variable with respect to giving. As an example, let's consider ZIP code. This category can be hard to break down meaningfully, as there are thousands of different codes. One way to get a handle on it is to try truncating it and looking at only the first number of the code. This gives us 10 groups that correspond to major regions of the country: 0 is New England, 1 is New York and Pennsylvania, 9 is the West Coast, and so on. If one chunk stands out as noticeably better than the others (something I've seen only rarely), I can score it as a 1 and score the rest of the sample at 0. If one chunk relates to noticeably lower levels of giving, I can set that one apart as 0 and combine the other categories into a group that scores as 1. Another thing that often works with ZIP codes is to divide them into those with only five digits recorded in the database versus those with ZIP+4 listed. Sometimes (though certainly not always) the ZIP+4s give more.

For a more complex example, let's take marital status. In my experience, the categories of this variable that are most likely to stand out are "single" and "unknown." That is, I've found that the people listed as "single" almost always make up a big group of folks who give considerably less than other people in the sample. The same is typically true of people whose marital status is unknown, compared with those who have marital status listed. Sometimes I'll lump these two poor-performing groups together into "single or unknown" and score that as 0, while the rest of the sample receives a score of 1 for that variable. Other times, I'll get a little fancier: I'll create different variables for each way of separating the groups. I'll usually do the latter if both "singles" and "unknowns" are poor givers but one is notably worse than the other.

Let's explore that fancier approach in a little more detail. Sometimes a variable presents us not just with two clear categories (generous and not-so-generous givers), but with three (generous, middling, and downright lousy givers). For example, take a look again at Table 7 and Chart 6, which show the relationship between year of graduation and giving:

Table 7

Class Year Quartiles	Total $ Given
1972 and earlier	$4,712,270
1973-1982	$908,502
1983-1990	$225,317
1991 and later	$65,055

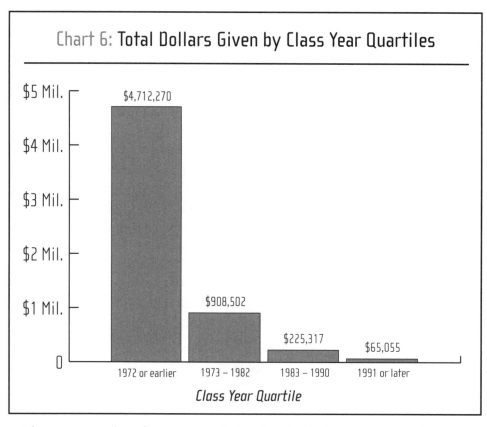

Chart 6: Total Dollars Given by Class Year Quartiles

(Bar chart with y-axis labeled in dollars: $5 Mil., $4 Mil., $3 Mil., $2 Mil., $1 Mil., 0)

- 1972 or earlier: $4,712,270
- 1973 – 1982: $908,502
- 1983 – 1990: $225,317
- 1991 or later: $65,055

Class Year Quartile

There are a number of ways you could handle this. For instance, you could contrast the class group of 1972 and earlier (scoring as 1) with the rest of the sample (scoring as 0). A more complex but more useful way is to separate out people who graduated in 1972 or earlier as great givers, and also to separate out those who graduated in 1991 and later as lousy givers. To turn this three-way division into a scoring formula, we actually *lower* the score for the poor givers: People in the 1991-and-later group would get a –1, while the 1972-and-earlier group would get a +1. The rest would, of course, get a 0.

Adding this type of variable to your scoring system means you can actually produce scores in the negative numbers. That is, if a record has a –1 value from a "lousy giver" variable and only 0 values from all other predictors we're using, the resulting score would be –1.

Adding depth and detail

I noted earlier that it's easy to make this step complicated. For now, you can manage a simple data mining project that will give you a useful scoring system just with the tools you've learned here. That scoring system can help you produce real results to improve your fund raising. But the tools I've described in this guide aren't the only ones available.

If you choose to learn more about statistics, you can refine your scoring system to be more precise and more powerful—and produce somewhat more accurate results.

Just to give you a glimpse of how this process can get more elaborate, let's talk about another element you might someday incorporate into your scoring system: weighting. Weighting accounts for the fact that some predictors are better than others at "discriminating" between good givers and not-so-good givers, and should thus play a more powerful role in determining the total score.

I don't want to confuse you with a complicated explanation, so here's a simple one that admittedly leaves out some details. To weight a 1/0 variable within a scoring system, you'd begin by computing something called the "correlation coefficient" between that variable and total giving. If the correlation is greater than .1 but less than .2, you would keep the variable's weight as we've already described—a 1 counts as a 1, and a 0 counts as a 0. If the correlation is greater than .2 but less than .3, you'd weight the variable by multiplying it by 2—so what we had designated as a 1 now counts as a 2 in computing the score. And so on for higher degrees of correlation. (My weights never get higher than 4.) This lets really important predictors play a greater role in the scoring system.

Stepping back a bit

Because this is a guide about statistics and data and how to use the former to make sense out of the latter, we've had to go into a lot of detail. I'm afraid there's no way around that. But after having delved into all this detail, I think it's important that we take a minute to step back and look at the big picture, and remind ourselves why we're going to all this trouble.

What all this work is about is helping you use statistics to uncover information in your database that can help your institution save money and generate lots more fund-raising revenue. Charts 16 and 17 give you a glimpse of the potential power of this information. Remember, all we've done here is combine three simple pieces of information that already exist in a database that contains huge quantities of information. And look at how combining just these three pieces of information has allowed us to separate bigger givers from smaller givers. What if we took the time to develop a score that combined 10 pieces of information, or as many as 30 or 40 pieces of information (as one of the schools I'm currently working with is doing)? Imagine how we could separate out the good giving "bets" from the poor giving "bets," all with a little probing into your database and a little manipulation of data using some very basic statistics.

Check out the scoring system on the cross-validation sample

If you page all the way back to Step 3 ("Import the file into a statistical software package and split it in half"), you'll recall that we took our file of 10,000 records that we originally imported into DataDesk and we split it into random halves of 5,000 records each. Since then, we've been working exclusively with the development sample of 5,000 records. We haven't even taken a peek at the other 5,000 records in the cross-validation sample.

Why did we do this? Why didn't we just do our search for predictors of giving with the full sample of 10,000? Here's a brief review of the argument we offered in Step 3:

> "When you do a project like this, it's easy to take advantage of the idiosyncrasies of one sample to generate a scoring formula/segmentation schema that looks great on that particular sample, but turns out to be not so great on another sample. So we want to hedge our bet. We want to see if the relationship between scores
> and giving we get in one sample looks as good (or almost as good) on another sample. If it does, then we can be confident we're headed in the right direction."

So that's why we go through this cross-validation process. Now let's do it and see what we get.

The first thing we want to do with our cross-validation sample (the one we haven't looked at yet) is construct a score for each record as we did in the development sample. So we assign a 0 or 1 to each piece of data for our three predictors and add up those numbers to make a score ranging from 0 to 3 for each record. Here's the frequency and percentage distribution of scores we end up with for the cross-validation sample:

Table 14		
Score	**Count**	**%**
0	1753	35
1	1804	36
2	1103	22
3	340	7
Total	**5000**	**100**

It looks remarkably similar to the one we got in our development sample (reproduced here from the previous step):

Table 13		
Score	**Count**	**%**
0	1709	34
1	1834	37
2	1119	22
3	338	7
Total	**5000**	**100**

That's a good sign. But what about the relationship of this score to giving in the cross-validation sample? Here's one way to look at it:

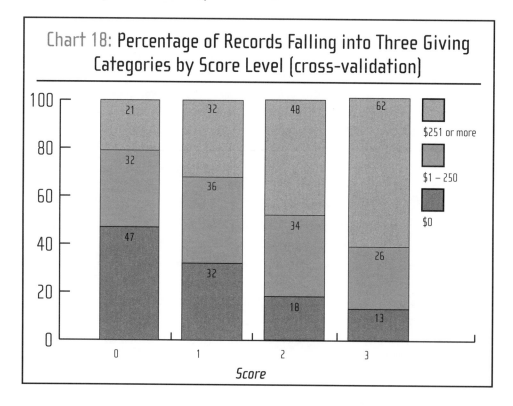

Chart 18: Percentage of Records Falling into Three Giving Categories by Score Level (cross-validation)

And here's another way to look at it:

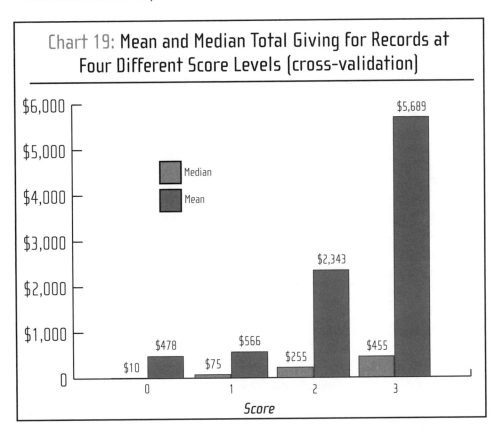

Chart 19: Mean and Median Total Giving for Records at Four Different Score Levels (cross-validation)

How do these charts compare to the ones we made earlier for the development sample? Take a look at these two pairs of condensed charts and see what you think. (The first one in each pair is from the development sample; the second in each pair is from the cross-validation sample.)

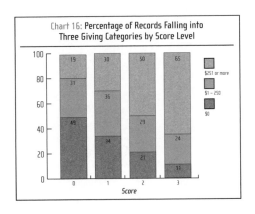

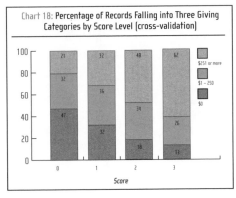

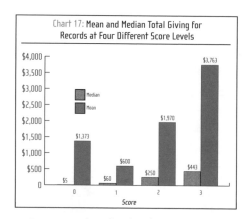

Chart 17: Mean and Median Total Giving for Records at Four Different Score Levels

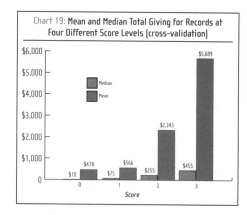

Chart 19: Mean and Median Total Giving for Records at Four Different Score Levels (cross-validation)

In comparing the development sample with the cross-validation sample, we could go into a lot of technical detail and hair-splitting if we wanted to. But why bother? It's clear that the scores work essentially the same way in the cross-validation sample as they do in the development sample. And that's what we want to see. That tells us we haven't taken advantage of some idiosyncrasy (or set of idiosyncrasies) in the development sample to end up with a scoring approach that works for that sample alone.

So what happens if we don't come up with a score that looks pretty much the same (as a predictor of giving) in the cross-validation sample as it does in the development sample? What do we do then?

Frankly, it's never happened to me. In the dozens of databases I've worked with over the last several years, the cross-validation score has always looked essentially the same as the development score. And I think that's a function of a couple of things: One, my clients and I are always dealing with large samples (thousands of records), so the sampling fluctuations we might see with smaller sample sizes simply don't appear. Two, we're very fussy about what we choose as predictors to include in a score. We look for differences that pass the "Whoa! Look at that!" test.

But if we did encounter a situation where the cross-validation sample scores looked markedly different from the development sample scores (either much better or much worse), I think the only solution would be to start checking. Are there some glaring things wrong with the way our file was constructed? Have we miscoded something differently in the cross-validation sample from the way we coded it in the development sample? And we'd hunt until we found the answer.

Test the scoring system on a limited appeal

Perhaps the best way to describe how to test a scoring system on an appeal is through an example.

In Fall 2000, I had the pleasure of getting a call from Randy Bunney, director of development research at the University of Minnesota Foundation, regarding an article I had written for CASE CURRENTS on data mining. We decided I would teach Randy data mining over the phone. Specifically, we decided to come up with a very basic scoring formula that would generate scores that could be imported into UMINN's database for some 40,000 people, 30,000 of whom were lasped donors and the remaining 10,000 of whom were recent donors.

Going through the basic steps outlined in this guide, Randy and I came up with the following scoring formula:

Score = (business phone good) + (home phone good) + (job title listed) + (married) + (born before 1948)

Each of the terms in this equation was a 1/0 variable, so the scores ranged from 0 to 5. Just to be clear, 0 meant that a person did not have a good business telephone number listed, did not have a good home telephone number listed, did not have a job title listed, was not listed as being married, and was not listed as having been born before 1948. A score of 1 meant that a person met one of these criteria but not the rest, and so on. (A note: We don't know whether the telephone numbers listed as "good" were actually working numbers in reality. All we know is that they were denoted that way in the database, and the database fields are all that we care about for the purposes of analysis. Even if the data themselves are wrong, they can still turn out to be good predictors for statistical purposes if they follow a pattern. I just wouldn't depend on having luck with those phone numbers in every case if I actually needed to call all these alumni.)

After scores for the 40,000 people were imported into the university's database, UMINN mailed appeals to all these people. The annual fund folks who were doing the solicitation had no idea what the scores were for any of the people mailed to.

About six weeks after the mailing, Randy and I did an analysis of the giving rate for each of the six score levels. The chart below tells the tale:

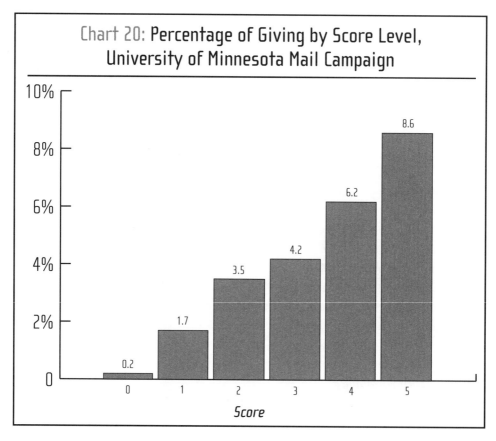

Chart 20: Percentage of Giving by Score Level, University of Minnesota Mail Campaign

What was particularly interesting about this test was that over half of the people who received the mailing had a score of 0 or 1. Guess who got the most attention from the annual fund folks for a second and third mailing during that fiscal year?

Applying what you've learned

In the appendix (pages 77–79) I've recommended some resources you can check out that should help you go beyond what I've covered in this guide. But now you've got the "stats" basics I think you need to start digging into your database and doing some useful analyses.

But as I said in the very beginning, what's really important here is not the statistics. The statistics are simply a tool—a means to an end. And the end—the goal here—is you and your advancement colleagues making better, more accurate decisions about your donors and prospective donors. For example, some basic statistics work could help you accomplish these things:

- If you're picking out promising donors to assess for major gift potential, you can determine which of the thousands and thousands of names in your database to submit for a wealth capacity screening.
- If your mailing list has 50,000 names but your budget is only big enough for a mailing to 30,000, you can figure out what portion of your "lybunts" (the people who gave last year but not this year) should get mailings on this round.
- You can identify which of your major donors your president and gift officers should be devoting their travel time to.
- You can decide who among your 60-and-over widowed alumni are most likely to make a bequest to the university, and target your pitches accordingly.

If this guide can help you do these kinds of tasks more easily and quickly, all the time you've spent trying to wrap your mind around this material about samples, variables, and relations among variables will have paid off handsomely.

Resources for further exploration

I'm delighted you're looking at this section. That means you're open to the idea of going beyond what I've offered in the body of this guide. And I think that's great.

Before listing some resources that can take you further along in data analysis and statistics, let's talk a little about where you may be heading in these two areas as part of your work in advancement. It may be that you're about to join the ranks of a new crop of professionals emerging in the field of fund raising. These "data analysts" are folks who are tantalized by all the information available about their donors and prospective donors and who get excited about exploring that data, possibly devoting a portion of their careers to this exploration.

As an example, let me describe someone I know quite well, even though I haven't met her face-to-face. Since she prefers that I not use her real name, let's call her Andrea.

I met Andrea over the telephone in Summer 2002. She's a prospect researcher at a major public university. She'd read some of what I'd written about data mining and was interested in its application to her own work. In Spring 2003, I began training Andrea over the phone on how to do data mining with a focus on major giving.

Like all the clients I work with, Andrea struggled a bit with the software and with the analysis. But what stood out about Andrea was her persistence and enthusiasm for the big picture. She was an outspoken advocate for data mining within her core development group and out among the development officers in the various schools within the university. She was bound and determined to get her arms around data mining and to make it a part of the advancement culture at her institution. As I write this, Andrea is taking her second class in what will be a year-long course in business statistics at the university. She has even approached her course professor about getting involved in data mining. In short, Andrea has taken data analysis far beyond what I have taught her, and far beyond the material I've included in this guide.

Maybe you're not quite ready to forge ahead like Andrea has with stats and analysis. But if you do want to dig deeper into the topic, here are a few suggestions:

- Read (or at least browse through) two books I recommend.
- Check out the Internet.
- Network with other professionals in advancement.
- Take advantage of the resources of your institution.

Let me elaborate.

Two books I recommend

I'll admit it; I'm a little weird. I actually enjoy reading books on statistics and research methodology. Yes, the vast majority of them are badly written and badly edited. (If that weren't the case, I wouldn't have expended the energy to write this guide.) But the topic of statistics fascinates me, and I'm always able to glean something useful from even the worst books.

Every now and then, however, I run across a book that stands out either because of its clarity and ease of understanding or because it treats a particular topic in a helpful and comprehensive way.

From the standpoint of clarity and ease of understanding, I recommend you take a look at *Statistics: Concepts and Controversies* by David S. Moore (W.H. Freeman & Co., 2000). I picked it up last summer and had trouble putting it down. The author (a professor at Purdue) explains concepts clearly; he uses interesting examples that involve a little drama; and more than once he made me guffaw. Take a look at it.

As for a book that deals with statistics for fund raisers, I haven't found anything. But I've found something pretty close. It's called *The New Direct Marketing* by David Shepard Associates (McGraw-Hill, 1999). Its focus is on direct marketers in the private sector, but many of the principles it lays out are directly relevant to our field. Most important, it covers statistics in depth from the perspective of making appeals and evaluating what sorts of predictors do and don't work. The downside is that it's long, rather expensive, and very unevenly written (because of multiple authors). Crystal-clear passages alternate with sections in which the prose becomes confusing, disjointed, and frustrating. Those flaws notwithstanding, I recommend it for the serious student of data analysis in fund raising.

Check out the Internet

This may seem like a no-brainer, but I'll mention it anyway. Get online and do a search on "basic statistics texts." You'll find a vast amount of free information. Yes, there are plenty of sites that sell books, but there are also scores of professors in schools around the country who have essentially put their courses online for anyone who wants to take advantage of them. It's fantastic.

Network with other advancement professionals

This is something I'm constantly encouraging my clients to do. If the subspecialty of data analysis within fund raising is ever really going to take off, folks just like you will have to network more than they're doing now.

There are lots of different ways to network, of course, but e-mail lists may be the easiest way. If you belong to FUNDLIST or PROSPECT-L, just put up a message saying you're interested in learning more about data mining and statistics and how they can help you in your job. I guarantee you will get lots of positive responses. The folks who subscribe to these two lists are some of the most helpful and cooperative professionals I've ever encountered. Ask for their help, and help them out in return if you can. You'll be glad you did.

Take advantage of the resources of your institution

Here I'm talking primarily to those of you who work in a college or university. If you do, you're surrounded by smart people and superbly good resources. Take advantage of them. For example:

- You have a library that probably contains lots of statistics books, and your reference librarians can borrow almost any technical book in the world for you.
- Data analysis and data mining may be topics that will cause your friends' eyes to glaze over, but I guarantee you that they won't bore some of the super-bright folks on your campus. Applied mathematicians and their students are intrigued by these sorts of projects. Talk to them about what you're doing. They may offer to help you out.
- Think about taking a course (or at least auditing one) on statistics or a related topic. Another client of mine signed up for a data mining course offered free on campus by a software vendor. My client said, "Honestly, a lot of it was way over my head and the instructor wasn't too hot, but I still got a lot out of it. It really got me thinking about our data in some new ways."

Now go have some fun with all this stuff!

About the Author

In 1993 Peter Wylie, now of Margolis-Wylie Associates, made a career change and became a marketing consultant to higher education. With a doctorate in industrial psychology, he had established himself as a specialist in helping business partners who had come into conflict. But he was losing interest in the partners and their problems and looking around for something else. He had a strong background in statistics and came across a publication for public affairs officers at colleges and universities that said most institutions of higher education had enormous databases but were ignoring what could be learned from them. Peter took his cue and set off to help university development departments to analyze data on their alumni and donors.

Margolis-Wylie Associates serves about 15 client institutions at any given time, analyzing which characteristics make a person likely to be a good donor and where to find those prospects. Peter's specialty is in training prospect researchers to develop skills so that they can perform this sophisticated analysis in house.

Peter's other books are *Problem Employees: How to Improve Their Performance*, Upstart Publishing, 1991; *Problem Bosses: Who They Are and How to Deal with Them*, Facts on File, 1987, Fawcett paperback, 1987; and *Can This Partnership be Saved*, Upstart Publishing, 1993 (Fortune Book Club Coselection, August, 1993).

Glossary

categorical variable: A variable for which one category of data cannot be measured as "more" or "less" than another. For example, the field PREFIX in a database has categories such as "Mr.," "Ms.," "Mrs.," "Dr.," and so on. It makes no sense to say that "Mr." is more than "Ms." or that "Dr." is less than "Mrs." Other examples of categorical variables are religion, blood type, and hair color. Compare to **quantitative variable**.

cross-tabulation (cross-tab, contingency table): A table that shows the relationship between two categorical variables. For example, a cross-tabulation might show the relationship between gender and enjoyment of watching televised football games. In that case, the table might show the percentage of males versus the percentage of females who say they enjoy this activity thoroughly, enjoy it somewhat, don't enjoy it at all, or have no opinion.

field: The "column" part of a spreadsheet file. "Field" is really just computer language for "variable"; a field designates a quality or attribute for which a value may be listed for each record in a database. In a database of people, fields might include UNIQUE ID NUMBER, FIRST NAME, LAST NAME, STATE, BIRTH DATE, GENDER, etc. Compare to **record** and **variable**.

hybrid variable: In this guide, a term used to refer to a variable that has categories in the form of both numbers measurable on a scale and values (such as words or symbols) that cannot be measured on a scale. An example in a donor database might be a variable for number of children. Numeric values would include "1," "2," "3," and so on, but there is also a non-numeric value of "missing." Note that "missing" means there are no children listed, but does not necessarily mean the individual has "0" children. Compare to **categorical variable** and **quantitative variable**.

1/0 variable: A variable that has two categories, labeled with the numbers 1 and 0. The assigning of the 1 and 0 is arbitrary. For the variable of gender, "males" might be assigned a 1 and "females" a 0, or vice versa. 1/0 variables can be combined algebraically to form scores, which is not possible for variables whose values are specified non-quantitatively ("alpha" categories).

outcome variable: Any variable whose value is to be predicted from another variable. Giving (e.g., whether someone donates to an upcoming campaign) is a typical outcome variable in fund raising. Compare to **predictor variable**.

population: The universe, or total collection, of records in a database, from which a sample is drawn. See **sampling**, **random sample**, and **systematic sample**.

predictor variable: Any variable used to predict the value of an outcome variable. For example, the presence or absence of a business phone listing in a donor database may be tested as a predictor of giving in upcoming campaigns (the outcome variable). If the predictor variable of business phone listing shows a statistical relationship to the outcome variable of giving, that suggests individuals with a business phone listed are more likely to make a pledge to a campaign than those without a business phone listed in the database. Compare to **outcome variable**.

proxy variable: A variable that appears to be related to an outcome when in fact it's simply another measure of that outcome. For example, if an institution awards membership in the "Silver Club" to donors who have given a lifetime total of $1,000 or more, then the variable of Silver Club membership is a proxy for giving. Using this variable to try to predict giving would not make sense because all Silver Club members are donors by definition.

quantitative variable: A variable whose categories are measurable on a scale, so that one category can be said to be more or less than another. Age is a quantitative variable because it's measured in years; age 50 is more than age 49. Weight is a quantitative variable, because 175 pounds is more than 174 pounds. Variables measured in dollars are also typically quantitative variables — that is, $1,000 is more than $999. Compare to **categorical variable**.

random sample: A specific subset of records drawn from a larger population in such a way that no one record in the population has any more chance of being drawn than any other record. The records in the random sample may then be used to estimate characteristics for the total population. For example, the mean (average) total giving for all

500,000 people in the database can be estimated from the mean for a random sample of 5,000 records. Compare to **systematic sample**.

record: Individual entries in a database that form the "row" parts of a spreadsheet file. In the examples described in this guide, each record represents a person listed in a donor database; for each record, individual values for that person's qualities or attributes are listed in various fields. In most donor databases, each record has a unique ID number. Compare to **field**.

sampling: A scientific technique used to estimate some value in a large population based on a small portion (sample) of that population. For example, sampling is used in political campaigns to estimate voter behavior in a population of millions of voters by drawing a sample of only a few thousand voters and asking them how they plan to vote. See **population**, **random sample**, and **systematic sample**.

scoring system (segmentation system): A method used to combine pieces of information in a database that are good predictors of a specific outcome. The scoring system is used to rank records with respect to their likelihood of performance on the outcome variable. In fund raising, the outcome variable might be donation to a future campaign. The scoring system would assign a number to each individual in a database to predict that person's likelihood of donating. If scores in the system go from 1 to 5, people with a score of 5 would be more likely to donate than those with a score of 4. The 4's would be more likely to donate than the 3's, and so on.

systematic sample: A sampling method that approximates a random sample. This method works particularly well if the population to be sampled is in the form of a list. The number of records in the entire list (the population) is divided by the number of records to be drawn for the sample. The quotient is called k, and every kth record is drawn for the sample. If you want to draw a sample of 5,000 from a list of 500,000, k would equal 100, and you would use every 100th record in the sample. Compare to **random sample**.

variable: Any quality or attribute on which people (for the purposes of this guide) vary. In a donor database, examples might include amount of giving, gender, age, state of residence, etc. Compare to **field**.

Index

A

age. *See also* DOB field
  as donor database variable, 7
  as quantitative variable, 23
  in relation to class year, 40
annual giving programs
  scoring systems and, 4
  statistics essentials for, 3–4
appeals, scoring systems and, 4, 73–74
averages, variable types and, 24

B

Bunney, Randy, 74
business phone, as donor database variable, 8
BUS_PHONE field, 9
  for database sample, 19

C

categorical variables, 23, 24, 83
  hybrid variables and, 24–25
  percentage distributions for, 28–29
  predictor variables, outcome variables
    and, 43
  summarizing, 25–27
causality, prediction *versus*, 58–59
charts, tables *versus*, 29
children. *See also* NUM_CHILDREN field
  as donor database variable, 61
class year quartiles

giving and, 65–66
giving categories summarized by, 41–42
PREFYR field summarized by, 39–40
contingency tables, 44, 83. *See also* cross-tabulation
cross-tabulation, 44–45, 83
  of EMAIL field and giving, 46–47
  of FRAT field and giving, 54–55
  of NUM_CHILDREN field and giving,
    51–53
cross-validation sample, 21. *See also*
    development sample
  frequency and percentage distribution of,
    69–70
  mean and median of total giving by score
    levels, 71–72

D

data analysts, 77–78
DataDesk (statistical software), 21, 31–33
dependent variables, 44
development sample, 21. *See also*
    cross-validation sample; PREFYR
    field; scoring systems; variables
  frequency and percentage distribution of
    scoring system for, 62–63
  mean and median of total giving by score
    levels, 64
  mean for TOTAL_AMT field in, 34–35

median for TOTAL_AMT field in, 35
DOB field, 9. *See also* age
for database sample, 16
donor database, variables in, 7–8

E

e-mail address, as donor database variable, 8, 61
EMAIL field, 9
cross-tab of giving with or without listing
in, 46–47
for database sample, 19
development sample analysis using, 43
1/0 variables for, 61
percentage distribution with or without
listing in, 45–46
predictive modeling using, 47–48
Excel file, of database sample, 14, 21

F

facts, variable summaries of, 26, 40
fields, donor database, 21, 83.
See also variables
FRAT field, 9
cross-tab of giving and, 54–55
for database sample, 17
development sample analysis using, 43
1/0 variables for, 62
percentage distribution for, 54
frequencies
for cross-validation sample scoring system,
59–70
for development sample scoring system,
62–63
of variables, 25–26
frequency distributions, 28
for PREFYR field, 38
FUNDLIST, 79

G

GENDER field, 9
for database sample, 16
giving
class year quartiles and, 65–66
mean, median analysis of predictor fields
and, 48–49
as outcome variable, 44
proxy variables for, 58–59
relationship between predictor variables
and, 44
giving categories
in percentage distribution report, 33–34

summarized by class year quartiles, 41–42
Greek membership. *See also* FRAT field
as donor database variable, 8, 61

H

HOME_PHONE field, 9
for database sample, 18–19
hybrid variables, 24–25, 83–84
percentage distributions for, 30–31
summarizing, 25–27

I

ID field, 8
for database sample, 14
as variable, 24
independent samples, 21
independent variables, 44
institutional resources, 79
Internet resources, 78–79

J

JOB_TITLE field, 9
for database sample, 19

M

mailing costs, scoring systems and, 4, 75
MAJOR field, 8
for database sample, 15
as variable, 24
major giving programs
scoring systems and, 75
statistics essentials for, 3–4
marital status
assigning scores to, 65
as donor database variable, 8
MARITAL_STATUS field, 9
for database sample, 16–17
percentage distribution for, 28–29
summarizing, 25–26
mean, 34–35
of e-mail address listings and giving, 48–49
extreme values and, 36
of Greek membership and giving, 56
of number of children listed and giving,
53–54
of state of residence and giving, 58
of total giving by score levels, 64, 71–72
median, 34, 35
of e-mail address listings and giving, 48–49
extreme values and, 35–36